# BLUE

## An Anthology Of Short Works By

## Authors From Inspirations Writers'

## Group, Thanet

*Happy Birthday, 2021*
*Thank you for all*
*your help!*

Published by Wayside Publications
Manston, Kent CT12 5AW

Paperback ISBN 978-1-9993528-7-5

# CONTENTS

Foreword

# FOREWORD

This has been a stressful time for every one of us. One even we, as writers with amazing imaginations, never dreamt of occurring in our lifetime. Thankfully, despite the pandemic, Inspirations Writers Group has continued to maintain its group cohesion—albeit by transitioning into on-line meetings.

We have wonderful members who are committed to continuing our decade-long tradition of supporting each other and sharing our work. It's what we do. We have welcomed new members online too, offering our friendship, support, and hope.

Now we step onwards with Blue, because it takes more than a pandemic to stop us writing! Like its predecessors, our Blue anthology continues in the same vein with an assortment of stories and poems from different genres. The one thing they all have in common is the word blue, or an image which is identified as blue, nestled somewhere within their words.

Nor is this our last anthology. After Blue, we will continue our Rainbow Series with Indigo, and later Violet, with plans for further genre-based anthologies in the future.

I would like to take this opportunity to single out one member of IWG for a special mention; Karen Ince has continued to provide support, guidance and editorial input in all aspects of our anthologies, despite health issues, since the creation of our first anthology *Red* in 2016.

I would like to thank all our members too. I am so proud to be part of this amazing, inspiring, strong group of people. You make me humble by your commitment and friendship.

Carol Salter
Chair—Inspirations Writers Group
2021

# A Broken Promise

## By Karen Hutchinson

"TIME to die." The bullet met centre of target, between the eyes. Her thoughts turned to her husband. How often had they sat on the bench watching the goldfish?

Too often.

Him leaning forward, nearly tipping the bench, unsettling her coffee mug. Never could sit still. He would perch, then shuffle to sit back on the bench. And there'd be the briefest moment when she relaxed.

He wouldn't ignore the blind fish.

Up and down, his bony bottom hovered over the bench before the call of the blind fish lured him to follow it around the pond. Time after time, it missed the floating pellets he'd lovingly sliced in half for it and dropped in front of its gulping maw. He would scoop the pellets up in his fingers, drop them, again and again, in front of the blind fish. To no avail.

Fifteen minutes. Why couldn't he ignore the fish and enjoy this slice of time with her? Fifteen minutes of joined camaraderie, calmness, while they watched his remaining five fish surface to feed in a lazy swirl of gold, white and red — their hungry mouths always gulping, gulping. The blind one rammed into the corners, mouth gobbling, surfing for pellet flotsam trapped in the swaying algae fronds. Its perpetual bumping against the concrete callused its mouth, frayed its lips.

Two years.

The blind fish managed to survive two winters. Three of the coldest months. And each spring she prayed he'd find the blind one, belly up, its torn mouth stilled.

Two long years she waited for him to do the right thing.

Hoping he'd see sense.

Since he retired and when the weather allowed, they'd sit on the garden bench by the pond. She'd drink her milky coffee, he'd drink his tea, and they'd watch the fish eat. He sat at one end of the bench where the curlicue of steel supported the thin wooden slats; she sat at the other, left a gap between them. If she cosied up to him

1

the slats bowed, creaked. He'd laugh and clutch the side as if she might fall through; as if the weight she'd gained was the contributing factor. He'd painted the slats a royal blue; not satisfied with two thick coats of gloss he went for the reassuring third.

Their sojourn by the pond was by no means relaxing. He hovered. Got up. Squatted. Followed the blind fish around the pond's edge, scooped out sodden fish pellets, waited for the precise moment to drop them in front of the torn mouth, only for the fish to veer the other way, or gulp, gulp, and miss each one as if to spite her.

"Stupid fish." He'd laugh, in his gentle way; he bore it no malice.

She longed for him to kill it. To scoop it up, smash its head against the side and put it out of its dark misery. Why let it drag out its existence in perpetual darkness, sucking the surface of the water day and night in the hope of snaring a morsel?

Time to die.

The fish with its needy mouth spoiled her fifteen minutes of outside harmony. She'd rather be sitting in a café by the window, people watching, sipping her latte with its fancy heart design. She preferred the sound of espresso gurgling, milk steam-heating, the background murmur, to his running commentary on the blind fish's failure to eat.

Fifteen minutes. Him and her.

Him with his tea and two biscuits—plain digestives—wrapped in a paper towel, folded thrice over and tucked in against his palm, as if to hide it from her. Sometimes he brought out a piece of raisin toast, the melted butter blotching the kitchen paper he'd wrapped it in. A childhood thing, wrapping his treat in a paper towel.

"It catches the crumbs," he told her when she asked.

She thought, why worry about crumbs in the garden?

They each sat at their end of the bench and watched the gulping mouths chase after the fish food. Mug in hand, he studied the blind fish's progress as it circumnavigated from one corner to the other—a rectangle map in its brain: the fountain at one end; the long edges; the corners where baby frogs clung, half-in the water, and avoided its scabby, flattened mouth. She urged it to be successful, to gobble up a morsel, so he would remain seated, satisfied he'd seen it eat something.

Finally, it died.

Hurrah.

He dug a dry hole between the buddleia and the rickety back fence, buried the fish and placed two of her largest ornamental stones on top of the smoothed down dirt so the foxes wouldn't dig it up. Years ago, a fox had tried to dig up their first cat but he scared it off and put a paving slab over its grave, thought better of it and added a second on top, then a reassuring third. A year later, he buried their other cat. It left him with only the fish to look after.

Two years she had sat on this bench with him, his retirement bench, having to rebuild an easy rapport, an understanding of how things must be; melding his free time into hers; always mending her ways, minding her tongue, saying nothing to pique him. He ate his biscuits, dunked them half at a time; her milky coffee drunk, his tea not started. He dunked, pondered, sipped his cooled tea. It took him ages to get to the biscuit dregs.

That's where they decided. On the bench. Offered their solution if the other became doddery, lost their marbles, needed a nappy day and night.

"That's not living," he told her. "I don't want to end my days in that way."

She wanted him to wheel her down to the sea at high tide and tip her in. The nearby steep slope to the prom might be tricky to navigate but he could manage it in stages. She hated heights; hated turbulence in an airplane, the crash of an empty stomach into gravity. At high tide there'd be less of a drop. The waves would pull her under, quick. Suck her down to the chalk, to the abrasive rocks, churn her against the bottom and spit her out miles away, job done. She wanted to be unconscious too. She'd stressed this over and over.

"Remember to knock me out before you tip me over."

The thought horrified him.

"I'm not asking you to bash me over the head. Just feed me an overdose of my tablets. I won't feel a thing when I drown."

If he wouldn't put the blind fish out of its misery, could he put me out of mine? The thought didn't sit well with her. He might let me linger, until I go gaga, spewing profanities when I'm out of my mind. He'll let me become an object of derision, somebody to be avoided, pitied.

Deep in her bones came the realisation she wouldn't be a kind, white-haired lady. He would. Be a nice old man.

Carers would give him the time of day; they'd listen to his ramblings interspersed by his soft laughter as he got to the funny part of his story but couldn't remember it right; they'd hold his hand before setting a mug of warm tea into it and pass him a whole biscuit. Iced or coated in chocolate, not a plain biscuit. The rivulet of crumbs down his jumper, spilling into his lap, ground into the carpet, wouldn't rankle with them.

God forbid if she ended her days in a home. The care staff might set aside the leftover biscuits—stale, broken, plain—just for her. She'd be abandoned all day, sat in a corner, alone, to stew in her thoughts. No kind words for her. No holding her hand to comfort her. Neglected, until she drew her last breath.

She imagined her final journey. Slumped in the wheelbarrow with its squeaky wheel, swaying side to side down the narrow slope to the sea, onto the swathe of concrete prom. He'd park her by the rusted warning sign—its picture of a person mid-dive with a black cross over it, in the language of the illiterate—not to dive in, the hidden rocks a danger. In her mind the sun shone, the prom was deserted, and grey-green waves crashed against it, sending fine, salty spray over her recumbent body. High above, a lone gull soared, silent. He'd jiggle the wheelbarrow upright and tip her over the side. No tears. No words of farewell. His cheery wave, enough.

At high tide the drop was near enough six feet. Six feet before the sea engulfed her. In her self-medicated torpor, the shock of the cold water mustn't rouse her from the last comfort of dying.

She'd stashed two bottles of her painkillers in her bedside drawer. Taken out the cotton wool ball and stuffed in more, filled it to the brim so tightening the lid crushed the top layer of tablets. Come the time, she'd stick her damp finger inside and scoop up the powder, lick it. She remembered the sherbets she had when so much younger, when she was fast on her toes; a catch her mother said, "You're a catch for any man."

A flash of gold tracked across the ceiling.

He'd waited two years for the blind fish to die.

4

She remembered the sick one after it: the white one that swelled so much its scales jutted out; blood from a wound at the end of its body streamed red and faded to pink at the end of its sweeping tail. It gulped, gulped, and missed the fine fish flakes he'd bought especially. Crumbled them between his fingertips as he followed the fish around the pond's edges.

"They're old," he told her. "They spit out the pellets. Maybe they're difficult to swallow." Scabby bits of pink, brown, and green fish flakes stuck to his fingertips, wet from dunking his biscuits.

Four fish, one on its way out. An Agatha Christie title came to mind, 'Then There Were None'.

What will we do when the fish are gone? When he has nothing to fuss over? When it's just us?

An over-riding compulsion to shove him as he knelt at the edge dribbling fish flakes to the stupid white fish, stopped her heart, then made it beat faster. Blood raced as she imagined pushing him headfirst into the pond, scattering the stupid fish every which way. Saw herself land on his back, her feet between his shoulder blades, weighing him down with all those extra pounds—he called them her spare tyres—he made jokes about since he'd retired. Could she watch his mouth gape and suck in fish food and spit it out in his last breaths? Could she?

Drown him in his pond?

The idea grew as he fixated on Whitey: the fish incapable of swallowing the smallest of flakes. Its swollen body hardly moved in the water. Pitiful. But he hadn't put it out of its misery. Too kind.

"The new ones will breed," he told her the day he brought home a dozen tiddly goldfish, a skip in his step on his way to the pond.

Something in her broke. She couldn't wait out the days for the three oldest fish to die. She couldn't sit on the bench, day after day; him following each ailing fish, drip feeding it sodden pellets or crumbles of fish flakes, recounting each failure, each near success. She couldn't bear any more of his acts of prolonged kindness.

Two years. She'd waited. Counted each sunrise, each sunset. Willed him to do it.

The spider's web in the corner became a cobweb. Her exhale made it sway. Its shadow flitted into a tiddly grey fish.

5

"Time to die." She exhaled the words in a silent whisper, with no movement of her lips or fingers. She raised her imaginary gun and aimed it at the head, between the eyes. A clean shot.

No sound.

No ricochet.

The mirror didn't shatter. An unsatisfactory ending.

Two years. Two winters. Three of the coldest months. Still alive.

He'd gaped at her with his soft eyes, his mouth opening and closing without sound as they wheeled her in backwards into the ambulance. She stared at him, shouting the words in her mind: You promised to kill me!

Every waking moment stuck in this corner she killed things, with her mind. It was the only thing she *could* do.

# ALBERT ESCAPES

## BY VALERIE ANN TYLER

ALBERT stretched and yawned. *Another day, just the same as yesterday and the day before that.* He felt sweaty and lethargic, and couldn't find any motivation.

Albert snuggled into his favourite spot on the sofa where he could admire the garden through the French doors. Dappled sunlight shone through the glass panes illuminating the faded brocade which seemed more uncomfortable as time went on. It had become stale and smelly in contrast to the aromas of disinfectant and bleach that now took over the household.

Frieda had always used essential oils before because they were kinder to her sinuses. Albert preferred the smell of tea tree, pine and geranium but Frieda, reassured by constant news that Domestos and Dettol were best to get rid of germs had changed her preference. Now she was spraying and wiping alongside using antibacterial hand wipes, gel and washing hands frequently. She had one thing to be grateful for, living in a Victorian property. *Thank goodness for brass doorknobs. At least they kill bacteria almost immediately. I wonder why they don't use them in hospitals. It would make so much sense,* she thought, as she dusted and polished and disinfected her way around the house.

Seeing the activity of birds was comforting, especially when one didn't get out much. The government had suggested one walk a day for exercise to ensure good health but the venturing out had lessened as time went by and Albert hadn't been out for the best part of three weeks. He was glad of the back garden though it was very small and not the same as walking a distance. He found himself pacing, head down, in a circle at least twice a day. It was becoming a habit. On the other hand Frieda had become restless and had cleaned every cupboard from top to bottom, bagged up old clothes and shredded piles of paperwork. It wasn't uncommon for her to say, "There, that's it!" as she stood back and admired her daily achievement.

Though the once-a-day walk and going out for food and medical supplies was permitted, most hadn't ventured out much at all because of the fear of corona virus Covid 19. Many had taken to ordering online. Only shops that sold essentials were allowed to stay open. Many businesses had closed and people were furloughed. Never in anyone's lifetime did even one person remember a period of isolation like this, though there had been rampant diseases and 'flus in the past. Even in World War II when people gathered in tube stations or down air raid shelters at least they had the company of each other. This lockdown didn't allow members of a family to see each other unless of course they all lived in the same house. People in nursing homes were not allowed visitors and many people were dying alone.

*This past month feels like a year's passed. It's hard not being allowed to meet up with friends and family. How much longer can this go on and why is it even happening? I wonder how others feel. Those on their own must be very lonely. It would drive me mad if I couldn't go out at all. At least there's the beach close by, but for those that don't live near I've heard they're not allowed to drive there.* Albert's thoughts were in sympathy for others as he tried to convince himself he was in a better place, though he missed his family.

Frieda felt lonely too. Of course, she wasn't on her own. She lived with Albert, but the lockdown caused by the pandemic had resulted in much higher levels of anxiety and depression than usual. He saw her reach for her pills so often now, and her hands shook. He wished he could find words of comfort but whenever he tried to speak she shouted at him frantically. She had what she called her nerve pills, and she had others for pain or inflammation like Ibuprofen. There had been an announcement on the news not to take Ibuprofen if you had symptoms of coronavirus as they had been found to lower the immune system. She had a stack of them — they were what she usually took when she felt a cold coming. Although she couldn't quite understand this statement, for now she would avoid them. This heightened her angst.

"For Heaven's sake can you just be quiet and leave me alone? You just don't understand how I'm feeling and I cannot even explain it myself so it's no good trying to talk. So stop it, Albert, just stop it. I don't want to hear your voice. I'm sorry, I don't want to seem mean, but it's beyond your comprehension," she blurted loudly, while stretching upwards, patting her hands around in the cupboard to make sure she hadn't missed anything.

There were bouts of uncontrollable sobbing when Albert tried to console her, so he had gradually started to restrain the sound of his own voice, holding his feelings and concerns close to his own heart.

Albert found the way she spoke to him degrading, but then unexpectedly contradictory to how she spoke at other times when she would walk over to where he sat, pat his head, and sometimes even stroke his hair tenderly with her long fingers. He was at her beck and call, only going out when her mood allowed; sometimes he felt like a prisoner and wondered if she did too, but he knew he'd never find out because she kept those emotions to herself.

*How long can a relationship last with no communication, tenderness, or warm embrace? And if she wants to rid herself of me, how will that happen?* thought Albert, knowing that he was already preparing himself for whatever came next and even beginning to get used to the idea, though not liking it.

Frieda had worn the same blue dress for three weeks. It matched the chair and a picture above it which displayed blue sky and a vast turbulent ocean. In fact, there was a lot of blue, including her mood of late.

"Well, it's not as if anyone's going to see me, is it?" she'd say to Albert, as though he'd asked her a question. She thought she knew his thoughts and felt judged by the way he looked at her with deep soulful eyes. He sometimes seemed wiser than her but even so he couldn't make her feel happy.

Today was different. For some reason Frieda entered the room looking like a proud flamingo, flamboyantly dressed in pink. She hadn't worn pink for a long time. Although it could have been yellow for all Albert knew. Albert opened his mouth to speak.

"Shh you don't have to say anything," she interrupted. Albert didn't know what had happened to his voice but since the new-found fear that Frieda no longer enjoyed his company even before lockdown arrived, no sound would come out at all, so she needn't have worried. Albert hoped this wouldn't be a lasting inconvenience. He remembered the last time they'd met up with friends Barbara and Geoff before lockdown and how his lost voice became the pinnacle of their conversation. He had felt embarrassed and frustrated.

"It's probably 'cos he can't get a word in edgeways," Barbara had said to Geoff when Frieda explained that Albert had temporarily lost use of his vocal chords. Barbara had put her hand in a position to shield one side of her mouth so that Frieda couldn't see. Geoff leaned to one side to get closer and smiled in his normal quiet manner. He was slim and a foot taller than his wife.

Albert liked Barbara; she came out with the funniest, sometimes sarcastic, remarks that made people giggle. She was short and slightly overweight before lockdown and was even more so now. This she had confessed to Frieda during one of the many zoom meetings that had become so popular, and which were never private when Albert was in the room. Barbara made fun around others but at home frowned a lot when standing on the scales before getting dressed. She was lighter without clothes and convinced herself that if she stood further to the back her weight went down by another pound. Her heels, which used to add height, were tucked away and her flat walking shoes took place of preference. Her belts were non- existent now, as was her waist. The information was explained enthusiastically on screen as she waited for a similar betrayal of self-evaluation from Frieda but there wasn't one.

Now that lockdown was over and everyone was excited about walking-out, two metres distance didn't seem such a bad price to pay. "We're going out today," Frieda said triumphantly, "and guess where we're going? Yes the beach, the beach, oh we're going to the beach." She burst into song—one she'd made up in the excitement of the moment. She had been a drama teacher in her younger days and possessed an operatic voice that she could turn on suddenly, startling people around her. Frieda's passion for operatic music surpassed her understanding of other people's tolerance for it. She danced around the room, her arms flailing, pulling the silk scarf from her neck to make patterns in the air while making time to glance at her graceful gestures in the mirror. Its silver frame matched her hair, and her curls imitated the carvings. For one moment she imagined an audience looking back in admiration.

Her attention was brought back to the present time when she realised there was only Albert watching. She quickly fetched the coats. She insisted that Albert wore his coat even though it wasn't cold. He cringed and grunted when Frieda pulled his collar up as though he was some kind of show piece.

*You can be so irritating sometimes. Grrr.* His teeth chattered.

But Frieda didn't notice. *We must be show-offs today, dress our best,* she thought. Then out loud she said, "Guess what day it is. I bet you have forgotten, and we are allowed out. We've won, it's over. We're back to normal." It wasn't, of course, but she lived in hope.

Albert wondered what normal was, what she meant by forgotten and what day it was but didn't bother to ask. Life with Frieda was far from what others classed as normal. He hadn't even had a decent meal for a while. He wished he could cook but knew it was impossible and Frieda wouldn't think it his place to do so. He had watched Frieda walk around with a pair of tatty socks on her feet. Before the pandemic she would never have dreamed of wearing socks with a skirt. Her head displayed a river of grey and white streaks as there was no hair dye in the house but even if there had been, he doubted she would have used it as she would be too frightened of having an allergic reaction and ending up in hospital. It seemed a lot that went in weren't coming out.

As time passed Frieda had become lethargic and wasn't quite so fussy about the cleanliness of the house so the hoover was abandoned and plates and dishes were left in the sink. *I'm glad it's not my job, I'd never be able to stack plates with such skill,* Albert mused.

He was glad to learn that lockdown had lifted but had never really understood or believed in it like everyone else. No one he knew had died but people had begun to realise the danger that surrounded them. He'd never thought about death before, but he sensed others' fears, mainly Frieda's. *I'll go along with whatever she says,* Albert thought to himself. He smiled to know the fear had subsided at least for today.

Frieda reached for the pills and swallowed them down quickly with a glass of water. Ibuprofen was back on the menu as the latest health announcement stated that it was okay to take it after all. Now getting out, breathing fresh air, and seeing other people was her main focus. Frieda closed the front door behind her, carefully turning the key in the lock. She turned back to observe its condition, thinking, *The old panels look like they could do with a wash or maybe even some paint.*

Albert walked in front but turned to stare at the door too, it had been a while since he'd seen the other side of it. He ached all over, his arthritic leg giving him pain. *I know it's because I've had no exercise, and there's really been no reason for it, but probably everyone else is in the same boat.* He tried to convince himself that it wasn't his fault. He'd tried the mini trampoline just for fun, but Frieda did not think that was amusing and had stormed in the room when she heard the springs squeaking. Her first reaction had been to laugh, then she started hysterically shouting, removing her shoes and throwing them at him.

"Don't be ridiculous! You'll ruin it. Get off, get off, it's really not made for the likes of you. You're too cumbersome. It…it's for ladies only," she stuttered. "Can't I have anything for myself without it being ruined? Ooohh, how I hate you sometimes!"

*God she could be so cruel. Why do I stay with her?* Albert had left the room before his anger could rise. He knew he'd regret it.

Anyway, what was the point of snapping with no voice? He'd never been called cumbersome before and considered himself slight compared to others. Now he knew for sure that she was confused.

Albert noticed that there was something very strange going on and his trust had started to diminish. He was suspicious of her sudden onset of happiness about this outing but was still looking forward to catching up with friends. "I have a surprise for you Bertie," she kept saying in a teasing, high-pitched voice as she strutted along with nose in the air as if trying to detect an unknown smell. Albert hated it when she called him Bertie, it was usually only when her friends were about.

Before they reached the slope down to the beach, Albert noticed that there were stalls along the front where none had ever been before. He didn't think anything much would even be open yet but here they were, all celebrating. There was a man on stilts and a clown riding a penny farthing bike. They both wore bright colours of blue and yellow stripes. He wondered if their overgrown hair was normal or whether it was a residue of lockdown. The café was open for ice cream made with real clotted cream from Cornwall. He hoped for that treat at least but the queue was looking unfavourable. Albert's favourite was blueberry. He remembered that once the sun melted it before he finished, letting it dribble down his chin.

"Look at him, just like a kid, making a spectacle of himself," Frieda had said to the others as if he wasn't there, but Albert didn't mind making a spectacle of himself.

*I can enjoy being the centre of attention, and if it makes people laugh, then I'm happy.* He had smiled smugly. Today he wondered why everyone still had to keep the two metre distance, weren't allowed to hug or touch, yet were allowed to pass an ice cream to each other.

Frieda hadn't been taking much notice of Albert but suddenly she turned and called, her pink shawl falling from her shoulders, "Come on Bertie."

*For God's sake woman, leave me be and stop calling me Bertie.* Albert had found a place to sit on the wall that ran along the esplanade. He ignored Frieda. He was tired of her dominance over him. He glanced across the beach to see if any friends or neighbours were about but couldn't see anyone he knew. He watched as people gave long illegal hugs to each other in places they thought they couldn't be seen. Some cried, and others laughed, but Albert couldn't make head nor tail of people's behaviour. He didn't feel like them at all. All he wanted was to breathe fresh air and feel sand under his feet. He had often been called unsociable and today it was true, but he missed the company of his real friends, those that behaved like him and understood his moods.

*These people all seem quite mad. Definitely unpredictable. Probably something to do with being cooped up for so long.* He scratched his chin. Then, just as if he'd taken Frieda's anxiety from her and placed it on his own shoulders for some reason, fear entered his being.

Out of the blue, a well-dressed woman approached him. She leaned towards him, stroked and smoothed his brown hair, then ran her hand down his neck. He quite enjoyed the affectionate touch but it bewildered him. He felt even more uncomfortable when she moved closer and her piercing blue eyes met his. He was unfamiliar with this affectionate attention from a strange female and a feeling of distrust emerged.

"There, there, what's the matter? What a gorgeous little sausage you are."

*Whaaaat is she talking about* ? His ears pricked up. Albert felt the hairs on the back of his neck stand up as he heard the words, then a loud voice bellowed from one of the stalls.

"Hot dogs! Hot dogs! Anyone for hot dogs? Sausage in a roll?" shouted a rosy-cheeked man with an eager look in his eye, staring straight at Albert.

Everything became clear to Albert now. A feeling of terror ran through him. He never noticed the ice cream in Frieda's hand and the cake with his name on it. He had forgotten his birthday.

"Hot dogs, hot dogs." He heard the man shout again, even louder. He knew what was going on. With the words still ringing in his ears he jumped from the wall, turned from the crowd and ran as fast as his short legs could carry him. He was running for his life. The pain in his leg quickly diminished as he saw the sea in the distance and, reaching it, felt the saltwater wash his body. Voices called his name but soon faded into the background. He knew he would never be like them and he was free to be himself again. Jumping over the surf, his paws scurried at the sand below and tangled the seaweed. Albert knew that he didn't need Frieda or any other human that didn't appreciate a dachshund; he could survive on his own and was free and safe as any other dog.

At least until dinner time.

## ALFIE AND THE OLD LADY

### BY ANNA SPAIN

ALFIE, age fifteen, sits at the living room table hunched over a textbook preparing for a school exam. The doorbell rings.

Mum shouts from upstairs, "Alfie open the door please. I'm busy with Beth."

On the doorstep is an old lady with a large grey cat. Alfie crouches down to stroke the blue-eyed cat with its large tufty ears. The old woman with dark beady eyes and red crimped lips asks for a glass of water.

"Mum," Alfie yells.

"Young man, do you need your mother's permission to speak with me?" She sighs and her words drift around the porch. "I chose your house because of the shiny emerald-green door—a little faded in places but more heart beyond it than the many grey doors along the road." Alfie doesn't know what to say and lets the cat distract him. It arches its body and fervently rubs around the boy's legs with a loud purr…rrr, purrrr.

"Does your cat follow you everywhere?"

"Maxie is always with me. He likes chopped up cucumber, if you happen to have any."

Alfie thinks it's weird. He gently pushes the front door to, walks up the hall and, with a hushed tone, he calls upstairs, "Mum! Mum, there's an old lady at the door with a big cat. She wants some water… and…"

Alfie's mum wonders what the fuss is about—an old lady wanting some water. "Okay, fine. Take them through the side gate to the seat in the garden. And a cat you said? I'll be down soon."

The old lady's voice zips down the light, open hallway of the semi-detached suburban house. "Thank you, Alfie. Your mother is kind."

Thoughts of home study have evaporated. "I didn't tell you my name," he stammers.

"Your mother called out your name. I maybe three hundred and four, but my hearing is as acute as ever and I've listened through many a door." A small grin seeps into her twinkling eyes. She shuffles through the front garden between a peony shrub with large, plump, magenta flowers, and a gangly forsythia bush at the end of flowering.

Alfie, slightly taller than her at five feet seven inches, sprints ahead before the pathway narrows to meet the side gate, then walks backwards, looking and trying not to stare. He bumps into the white gatepost and stops. "What? You can't be. The oldest person is one hundred and twelve."

The old lady peers into Alfie's hazel eyes. "Not everything is as you expect. Maxie and I count our years as one. If you add our ages together it's somewhere around three hundred. And you really should get your facts straight. The woman in Japan is one hundred and sixteen, and she looks much older than me. I am very thirsty. That glass of water please."

Alfie thinks the old lady must be mad, there is no other explanation. He walks through the gate into the garden, then into the kitchen to get a glass of water. Meanwhile Maxie walks stealthily into the house and up the stairs to find Mum and Beth in the bedroom. The seven-year-old girl grins, her deep brown eyes light up—she stretches out her taut arms and hands, arches her back and kicks her feet. Mum's body tenses as the cat jumps onto Beth's wheelchair. Maxie pushes his soft muzzle into Beth's face, and she squeals with delight. "Mummy, nice cat."

Mum releases a sigh, leans back into the bedroom armchair and breathes deeply. For a few moments all Mum can see is paws, a large fluffy tail and ears that are incredibly large.

15

The old lady drinks the water and talks with Alfie as they sit on a wooden bench in the warm spring sunshine. "When did your father die?"

Alfie's face pales, he lowers his head and picks the ragged skin around his nails. He mumbles, "How do you know?"

"There are jobs to be done out here. The fence needs fixing, the guttering needs cleaning out, and there are a lot of weeds that will soon choke the lovely plants and flowers. Your mum is busy with your sister, you're studying, and Mum insists that you go out with your friends." The old lady speaks in a flat, matter-of-fact voice, soft as old, waxed leather, without sentimentality.

Alfie thinks it is none of her business, coming round here uninvited; he holds back from being rude as his Mum would be mad if he wasn't respectful. Where is she?

He replies, "Yeah, something like that. You seem to know a lot. Do you live around here?"

"I'm visiting."

A myriad of years and wisdom smile through her eyes. Alfie doesn't notice as his dark brown hair flops over his face, a safe place to hide from large, searing emotions.

"I'm Mrs Doogdab."

Alfie looks up at the rhythmical words—he plays with the sound in his head. *Dooog-Dab, dib-dab what a hat, ancient lab with a cool cat, Doog-Dab-bad-boy-rap.*

Alfie reasons that she probably wouldn't know about rap and sits in silence until he says, "Mum will be down in a minute."

"Not for a while yet, Maxie is up there with them."

"Beth doesn't like cats. One scratched her once. I'm surprised she hasn't screamed the place down."

"That cat wasn't well mannered. Maxie loves children, especially if they have disabilities. They will get on just fine."

Alfie wonders how she knows so much about them and looks at her closely. The old lady wears red leather shoes with a large strap and a shiny gold metal buckle. By her side is a large, worn, mustard-yellow bag which seems heavy. Maybe she's been shopping. The old lady opens the bag, reaches inside and takes out a cloak. She shakes it out, throws it around herself and disappears for a moment in garden-greens and red. Enrobed apart from her

16

head, she creates a flamboyant contrast to the Miss Marple type character that his granny likes to watch on the telly.

Alfie swings his legs, looks down at the ground and is about to get up to get his Mum. Then the old lady takes off her red, wide-brimmed velvet hat and shakes out her long, feather-soft, white, wavy hair. It billows out light as a cloud around her head, making her look less ancient.

"Alfie, if you could make a wish right now what would it be?"

"That's easy. For my dad to be alive."

"Of course you would. And your second wish?"

"That Beth wasn't disabled and Mum could do more normal stuff. I love Beth, but it's hard."

"And for a huge wish, anything at all no matter how fantastical."

Alfie's face brightens as the topic moves away from the deep and personal.

"Do you mean things like being famous, and saving rhinos, and everyone having enough to eat?"

"Yes, that sort of thing."

"At school we discuss a lot of stuff, and now it's all different because we can't go to school because of this virus. Sometimes I want to think about it, and other times I don't. Mum says I can join a climate walk when we're back at school."

Mrs Doogdab gets up to go and tells Alfie she will leave him a blank storybook. Now he just wants her to go, how can it be a storybook if it's blank? It's stupid. She explains, "Write down the one big wish and the consequences; imagine it's a pebble thrown into a pond—how far out and to whom would the rings travel? Choose well young man."

Maxie walks into the garden and sits at Alfie's feet then rolls over and purrs. He whispers, "Maxie, cool cat, this is all a bit weird. Do you really want some cucumber?" The cat gets up, walks to the kitchen, and stands by the fridge.

While Alfie is in the kitchen, Mrs Doogdab leaves through the side gate. Maxie eats every piece of diced cucumber, licks his lips, winks at Alfie then walks out of the door just before Mum runs down the stairs. Beth walks down the stairs behind her and throws

17

her arms around her brother. Rivulets of joy run down Mum's face and pool at the corners of her mouth.

Alfie looks at his Mum, mouth agape, speechless, while Beth jumps and runs around the garden laughing.

"I don't know what happened. I fell asleep and woke up when the cat pawed at my arm—I looked up and saw Beth standing. I don't know whether to call a doctor, a vicar or do nothing at all." She looks around and, with panic in her voice, "Where have they gone?" Mum rushes out of the kitchen door and through the side gate. There is no sight of the cat or an old lady. On the path is a book—the title page says 'Alfie'. On the first page are large, scrawled words.

*Your first wish is not mine to give,*
*The second wish I granted.*
*Now the choice is yours—*
*Wish very big as the whole world is counting on it.*

## BEHIND THE CURTAIN

### BY KAREN LEOPOLD REICH

MORNING. Creeping into the kitchen next door to slap a heavy scuffed kettle on one of the gas stoves—a communal domain, but usually free of the burly male residents until later. There will be the thick-stockinged, kerchiefed babushka sloshing her ashen-coloured mop around, probably bemused at the sight of any young woman in this place, let alone a foreigner, but wise enough to keep her counsel. At most, she may grunt a wheezy hello, but only if I say something first. No more. Safer that way.

Despite the cleaner's daily efforts, it is a grimy, greasy place. Unwelcoming. Cheerless. Graceless, like the wide streets outside, forever coated in a thin layer of mud and motor oil that swallows up the grinding, straining buses and trolleys, spattering them to dust colour. So misted over from overcrowding and lack of ventilation are they, that you can only recognise them by their outer shape as they lumber past amidst the ubiquitous, military-issue lorries and tankers. Even the falling snow only emphasises Moscow's dinginess before being corrupted by it.

I rescue the boiled kettle and lug it back to the room I share with the other girl on exchange, the babushka swiping at my footsteps with a sniff. Tea to start the day, a small pinch from our hoarded packet to add to yesterday's cold dregs in the jam jar, and then hot water on top. You can keep a tea brew going for days that way, I've learned. They say that is how a samovar worked: the tea concentrated in a tiny pot on top, from which you'd draw just a few drops into your cup, and then steaming water from the showy urn to fill.

I imagine a Chekhovian setting with landed gentry gathered round a grand table and a proud-polished silver samovar, where the tea would probably be fresh each time. I've never really seen a proper samovar, only the hammer-and-sickle stamped metallic version in the foreign currency shops to tempt tourists, or a prop in a stage production, but it must be elegant.

We don't even have a tea pot, and what we drink is standard gunmetal 'chai', unless we can find the sought-after Ceylonski. Also, unlike any Chekhov character, we add milk from our cache on the windowsill. Coffee would be nice, but instant coffee here is like gold dust. Something to bring from home, if you can get it through customs.

I slice a wedge of black bread and lay some window-chilled curd cheese on top while my roommate reaches for her salami, then we wipe away the crumbs and rinse our mugs in the bathroom before going about our day, which may take us in various directions, dictated largely by study and provisions. Today we have to be at the Language Institute for a ten a.m. class.

We live in the Mining Institute's student residence, however illogically. This is our base, our shelter in the massive, intimidating expanse of Moscow. This is where bureaucracy has deigned we should have our moorings, despite our having nothing in common with anyone else here, unless you count the fact that the next floor up is full of other foreigners, but they are Vietnamese and drive everyone away with the rank smell of fish that permeates the whole level.

We don't need fish to set us apart. We are given a wide berth for different reasons; everyone is shy of the consequences of being seen or heard with a Westerner during the Brezhnev era.

Everyone, that is, except our next-door neighbour, who even we can sense is here to keep an eye on us. Murat will tap at our door to ask how we're getting on and make conversation long enough to steal a quick glance around, taking note of anything out of the ordinary or whether one of us is out. He looks too affluent and too slightly built for a career in mining—unless he's planning to run the accounts for a company one day—but he has just the weaselly and ingratiating manner of a spy. Or so we've decided. The Central Asian laugh and inscrutable expression only contribute to that assumption. However nice it would be to have a friend here, we've never really trusted him. We are in such a contained environment and so conspicuous in this location that he just seems like more of the general surveillance on offer.

We were completely clueless the first month. It never occurred to us that the box radio bolted into the desktop of the room couldn't be switched off because it was meant to be a constant listening device. It was that long before we learned to write notes or speak in code to one another, before we started to notice who might be hovering outside the door, or in the same metro car. Mindfulness doesn't come naturally, not to the young and secure. Now, though, we know better than to say anything about who we might be meeting or where we might be going besides the Language Institute. My roommate is probably seeing her friend later, especially as they might be planning a weekend, but she wouldn't dream of mentioning it here. She really likes him, and the last thing she wants is for our 'minders' to pick up on anything.

As we head for the underground, I wonder whether we aren't overly dramatising the cloak and dagger thing to lend a thrill to our otherwise flat routine. People back home would think us silly; but then, thinking back to that initiatory photo session, I concede this is a different place.

The demand for photos was an early induction into Soviet life. I was directed on arrival and as a matter of some urgency to a photographer's studio in the district, almost as if it were a vaccination centre, without whose certification I'd not be admitted anywhere. I remember how bewildered and foolish I felt, unsure whether I'd understood the dean's office properly. Why would anyone insist on a professional photographer when there must be an automatic booth in a metro station somewhere?

At the photographer's I was amazed to find a large waiting area and a crowd to fill it. The process would take hours, not minutes, and the thought of a photo booth plagued me with renewed exasperation. Why was everyone so utterly resigned to shuffling away their day? I gazed dully and resentfully at them, so many black and white shadows of lives repressed and regimented into meaninglessness. Better than short-ending that life in some gulag, I suppose, although the two versions seem to differ only in degree of despondency. Many had their nose in a creased paperback, retrieved from a back pocket or a satchel. Never seen so many booked noses outside a library, suggesting that having a collection of poems or short stories on one's person was as much a reflex as having a door key when going out.

When it came my turn, after an eternity unrelieved by fiction, I was asked how many prints I wanted. Two? Four? They meant how many dozen! I finally went off smouldering with a sheet of at least twenty little black and white me's. Within weeks there were none left.

In the Soviet Union you have a lot of IDs. In the Soviet Union people keep files on you.

Before coming here I never saw myself as defined by more than a driving license, or possibly a student card.

This is a massively scrutinised world. Your pass—or *propusk*—is everything, and not just to get into the institute. I can't get past the beady-eyed pensioner on the front desk at my lodgings without showing the special photo-validated residence card over and over again. No matter how I stand out among the residents, no matter how often I've been in and out the same day and greeted her, the same 'Propusk!' command will stop me in my tracks. Needless to say, that is also the case at the Lenin Library and the Tretyakov Gallery reading room, and anywhere else of public significance where I hope to gain access. Mercifully, not when I try to visit my

21

old Russian teacher's family in their block of flats, but then someone will still be keeping watch. Every place has its Murat.

I get the impression I can't go many places without being noticed, checked, and monitored. I suppose that should be quite an ego boost, but it has the wrong sort of edge on it. A lesson in there somewhere.

I was so unnerved at being treated like a suspect to start with that I made a point of registering with the embassy. I wanted someone to come looking for me if I was marched off to the Lyubyanka. Ironically, the embassy staff weren't bothered about more than whether I intended to use the commissary (which I couldn't), and whether I hoped to join the film club (which I didn't and anyway couldn't). To them, I was a non-entity. So I left, grateful for permission to use the diplomatic pouch for mail at least, which remains my only safety line.

We are pulling in to Park Kultury, the stop for our institute. Just a couple blocks' trudge from here, once we're out.

"Careful! Doors closing!" rasps behind us, dissolving into the whirr-whine of another train approaching on the opposite platform. We burrow into the bulk of a dark, shabby crowd, and are borne along by it, absorbed by the search for signs to the right exit. Only as we are about to negotiate for footing on the escalator do I vaguely make out the slim gleam of handsome grey and black granite tiles beneath our feet. The rest of the interior fades like a cavern behind us as a series of torch-shaped lights ticks off the long surreal moments of ascent to another uninspiring session with our tutor, itself another tick on a discouragingly long calendar stretch separating us from normal life and home.

Clearing the brim of street-level, we move from under the coffered, radar-like dome and spill out onto the pavement through the one door that opens (crowd-control). Eventually, we pick a path over slippery worn snow and slushy ice that Russian so aptly calls *slyakot*, and head for what is intended as instruction. I am glad for my newly acquired rubber boots, Polish-made, that I picked up in that enormous department store known as GUM near the Kremlin. (Pronounced Goom, the letters stand for nothing more entertaining than 'State Department Store', typically. The shops are only identified generically).

We pass muster with the *dezhurnahya* at the door (concierge sounds too grand), who nods at our open-palmed *propusk*. Then we proceed up the bald wooden steps to the first corridor, on to another, a sharp turn, steps down, through the smoking corner, steps up, and finally beyond to our appointed classroom, ushered along by a faded, zig-zag parquet nodding like a broom action that sweeps other students away.

They won't talk to us either. Ours are private classes with one and the same woman, week in, week out. Although we enter the building like everyone else, travel the same eccentric circuit and queue at the same bursary window once a month, we might as well be vacuum packed and sealed in plastic. Not even the occasional foray into the student cafe produces anything more than carefully controlled curiosity. Everyone has too much to lose. The young people here are the darlings of the elite, and their time at the institute is the ticket to much-coveted jobs as interpreters and translators with the Foreign Ministry, if they are boys. Probably even diplomatic posts later on. The girls are in the teaching college, where they will qualify to teach Russian to foreigners, which also implies special privileges and possibly even choice assignments.

Such a paradox that life as a foreign language student holds so little opportunity for us to speak the language! We are pariahs on two counts: we are girls in translation, and we come from a cap country—that is, the antagonistic capitalist world. No one who aspires to the brilliant future the Party promises would dream of jeopardising it by making overtures toward us, not even to practice their English. Not with all the well-primed eyes and ears around just begging for something to inform on about a rival, as a means of getting ahead.

Let's face it, the two of us can't even talk naturally in our own room.

What is anyone to make of it? Tracked and traced on the one hand yet treated as though we don't exist on the other. Even a virus has more of a life.

I feel so wasted, so empty! Part of me can understand my roommate letting herself drift into a relationship, even if she is risking a lot, both for herself and for him. He studies here! They behave like total strangers within these walls, of course, but how long before they give one another away? Or, God forbid, I should betray them somehow! And yet, how romantic it must be to discover feelings for someone when there is so much at stake! To explore that untraveled dimension here in these severe surroundings, rather than back home where a heart need not be guarded! How does it happen that inner torrents of emotion are loosed in a world of suppression?

An image of docile booknosers flits to mind…

I just seem to clock in and out of these days of confinement with a dictionary as companion, and however much I do love the intricacies of Russian, I could never describe them as the intimacies of passion. The most non-linguistic excitement I've experienced so far has been to have a lifeguard at the outdoor Moskva pool offer to swim with me in the restricted training area. Of course, I'm keeping myself for the fellow back home, but the 'trainer' does seem nice. My boyfriend never wants us to do anything together outside; he's obsessed with writing his thesis. He's been writing it for years, and, anyway, he doesn't really go in for sports.

I like it when people stay in shape, and I do love the water, especially in that untrammelled, central, walled section of the pool where you can do blue lengths to infinity. Steam rises against the frigid air temperature, smudging and erasing the figures of casual bathers in the outlying, shallower circular basin, and there is a delicious sense of defying both reason and season. We have it all to ourselves—free, yet surrounded.

"Good morning," I say to our instructor as we enter the room and I take my seat, noting the immediate curl of anticipated boredom across my roommate's upper lip. Two hours ahead of us and months still to go. Today will be the usual rote translation from some approved article, nothing rousing or controversial or uplifting. Or original. Filler. Tick.

\* \* \* \* \*

I'm staying on the surface this time, braving the bus. It's more entertaining than the underground, if less efficient, because at least I can see where I'm going and hear what people are saying. I'll ride past colossal red tributes to the Party and Soviet labour, interspersed with repeated invocations of 'Glory!'; past sombre shop fronts displaying work clothes or pickled cucumbers; past hairdressers, the mere designation of which produces more flourish above the entrance than any styling to be had inside. I must have chosen the wrong time, though, judging by the crush, the disagreeable squash of flesh affording me no more than a blurred, cubist view this time.

Fortunately, the stops are announced, so there is still a chance of knowing when to pry myself loose. Besides, if it comes to it, I can always ask. (They have a saying here that the language will get you as far as Kiev.) Actually, I spend so much time on overcrowded buses that the one I speak is beginning to sound like the old ladies who pad out the seats, though I don't aspire, like them, to be this nation's conscience.

The other day a pack of them were screeching in collective rebuke at a teenager in a mini-skirt. "Have you no shame, girl?" "SHAME!" "My God, how can you make such a spectacle of yourself?" "The horror!" I was alarmed at the racket and didn't know where to put myself. The girl slinked off with a smirk. Actually, the mere thought of baring my legs in this cold gave me goosebumps. Head down.

Another time they will be policing children's welfare. Any grown male who fails to leap from his seat for a parent boarding the bus with a child will have the harpies come down on him pitilessly, regardless how brutal a shift he may just have completed or how heavy his bags. What harm could come to the impossibly insulated squidget, so swaddled as to scarcely resemble human form, is beyond me, but the demand is not negotiable. Children always sit. The Russians won't hear otherwise.

Today is unremarkable so far, except possibly for the whiskered man further down towards the front who seems to have an unusual amount to say and a poor sense of balance. Surprisingly, the coven either side are actually guiding him into a seat and turning a deaf ear.

For once I wish they would do more. I need to squeeze past him, which I'd rather not, but my stop is coming up.

Release, and in more ways than one.

This is a special spot. As I walk past the little park and turn right into Lavrushinsky Lane, the storybook mood envelopes me like the Tretyakov facade itself in its horseshoe embrace. My library pass shunts me beyond the queue of visitors directly into the galleries, where I always feel I have to pay my respects to the collection before wandering on to the academic annex.

I have my favourite rooms—those boasting late nineteenth- and early twentieth-century Russian painting—and I could blissfully hover in their orbit all afternoon, but I would get no work done. I am still researching the paper I have to submit after my return, having settled, somewhat provocatively, on the general area I want to explore.

A very serious business, this paper will be seen to justify my time abroad and to demonstrate acquired language skills by being written in Russian. Back in our previous life we were advised to consider linguistic themes, which, at best, might accommodate a more appetising snippet of literature to demonstrate targeted aspects of Russian. However, no one is supervising us here, still less enforcing any theme, so I am not taking that as an obligation. The classroom experience has been so stultifying that I have no interest in anyone's linguistic analysis, however sugared. Either this strange, ponderous Soviet wilderness has ground out any spark of inquiry in me, or it has propelled me into another, ulterior realm of sensation. I have turned to Irina for advice, and she has sent me here.

Ira is the cousin of my old Russian teacher at home—a louder, lustier, plainer version—and she has befriended me. She is a struggling book illustrator, married to Vanya, who himself strains to glean a livelihood from restoring old icons and church frescoes when he is sober. Neither are members of the privileged Art Academy, despite Vanya's talent clearly having been recognised. They subsist with no decent art materials of their own or access to official exhibition space (all the exclusive preserve of Academy members). They live boxed in by easels, and tattered art books, and stacked canvases in the poky flat they share with their two kids, yet both throw their door and their hearts open to me, as well as an over-generous table. I know they get help from Ira's ex-pat cousin, but I'm embarrassed they feed me. A cup of tea would do, and then we could concentrate more on real things. I am fascinated by what they do and know.

They introduced me to turn-of-the-century Russian art, which turns out to be a treasure trove. One of Ira's favourites is Petrov-Vodkin, for example, who has a major work, his 'Red Horse', hanging here, one of my regular ports of call. The rapturous, primitivist depiction of a lithe adolescent male astride a towering crimson mount by a lake of teal waters while another male, waist-deep in the lake, leads a nearly submerged white horse toward the shore. Exuberant, lyrical.

Petrov-Vodkin has another dazzling red horse, flying above mountain tops, which he painted over a decade later. And Roerich, better known in the West, also has alpine scenes of exaltation. Artists wielding a vivid, original language of their own who suggest a Russian portal to the sublime that is practically akin to religious iconography—that luminous tradition that has transported Russian Orthodox worshipers for millennia.

The world's foremost acclaimed icon is also here, in a specially designed viewing chamber: Andrei Rublev's great 15th-century 'Troitsa'—the sacred and doctrinally eloquent Trinity, magnificent, yet disarming in the distinctive soft jades and topaz blues of the archangels' robes.

Masterpieces escort me. A fur-shrouded prophetess upon a thronged snow sledge; Christ expended in the wilderness; golden birch groves and cloud-mottled lakes; Madonna dark in a carriage; a sun-pink girl with peaches; a jewelled swan princess...

The Tretyakov library offers me at least the chance to record something of this. I consult the books, take notes, and order copies of reproductions, resigned to them being in black and white. I scavenge for slides or postcard facsimiles or catalogues in the foreign currency shop.

Russian art has to be what I will write about, a domain that is as rich and voluptuous, sonorous, and nuanced as the idiom I'll use to describe it.

Choosing which painter and which work is my current dilemma. Today I will read about Vrubel, a romantic and a symbolist, originator of Russia's Art Nouveau, master portrayer of the Virgin and the Demon, and, tragically, a man who lost his sight before he died. How cruel and agonising a fate for a man of vision. The world mourns over Beethoven's hearing, but I ache for this

27

artist shorn of his art before the world at large could even know him.

* * * * *

Last days now. After nearly a year of sloshing through life on hold, I am crossing back to the other side of the curtain.

I've journeyed the last of the institute's friendless serpentine corridors, gagged on the last acrid fumes of disinfectant by the ladies' and performed the last arid exercises in translation by the book.

I have compiled the material for my paper. Future exchange students may blame me after what I've produced, when they are denied the laxity I've enjoyed, and I am genuinely sorry for them, as their stay will be strait-jacketed enough. For me, though, this process has acquired its own personal syntax, and the tale has been woven from promptings I cannot ignore.

I wonder what my roommate decided on. Probably something safe. She made herself so scarce toward the end that the subject never came up. She packed off at the first opportunity, only too conscious of the lack of any future for her and her friend, and tormented by the glum knowledge, while she stayed, that prolonging the inevitable would simply make things more difficult. She leaned hard on common sense and the undeniable appeal of the comforts and prospects at home, then moved quickly before she could change her mind. A practical girl, she's probably been revelling in pizza and barbecues and shopping sprees since, lapping up the adoration of her doting parents and letting friends spoil her at some seaside that is far more civilised than where we were allowed to take ourselves outside the oil wells in Azerbaijan.

I could be doing likewise. It's not that I haven't been missing all that. I have someone waiting for me too, who has been more than patient, though he has been running thin on supportiveness lately and keeps demanding to know what's keeping me. To think how I would have welcomed that months back! (I'd love to believe it's absence evening the scales.) At the moment, though, I'm almost resenting his interference. He'd never forgive me, but, if I'm honest, I have to say I'd happily stay on for another couple of months, if I could. In spite of everything that terrified and tested me to start with!

It helps that I've claimed the last rubles from my stipend, which, together with some small earnings, has given me plenty to keep going. It helps that I have the room with the miners all to myself and that even Murat leaves me in peace now.

Yet it's not about being on my own. It's about owning my being.

It was my decision to take up Russian back in university, when it made no sense to anyone. It was my decision to do a degree in it and to go on to translation and to this place which made me shudder. It has now become my decision, consciously or unconsciously, to have this shuddersome place help me graduate to another truth. To commune with what the Russians revere as their *dusha*, or spirit.

I have learned to trust a rude, gruff metropolis. I have even come to like it, the way one grudgingly comes to appreciate the coach who pushes us hardest. The monolith is not just weight and authority, and the grey-grown shuffle is not only about frustration. This has been the story of beauty in the beast.

When, in one of countless dismal queues, time first slowed past irritation to show me the wild burst of floral jubilation in a simple headscarf, I sensed a lid was peeling back.

When I eventually lifted my gaze from the mud and street slush to rows of central Moscow edifices in fairytale pinks, yellows, pale greens, and turquoise, I felt the tingle of a child's gingerbread delight.

When, after one especially lacklustre class, I dragged along the platform at Park Kultury underground, locked into the eye-level moment and in no hurry to go anywhere, a whole palace of marble, bas-relief sculptures and candelabra was revealed to my incredulous vision, as though a fog were lifting. And a fog has been lifting. Not just there, not just in other spectacular metro stations either.

I now stand in open acknowledgement before St. Basil the Blessed in Red Square, and I tremble with wonder at all that is rakish and phantasmagorical in its cupolas. I slip inside. Deep within the stillness, ancient icons chant in carmine, viridian, and gold, touching chords of devotion to purest beauty and light.

And I know that when life picks up again back home in the autumn, I will be at the Fine Arts Academy. Let me not die blind.

## BLUE QUIVER

### BY KAREN LEOPOLD REICH

BLUE quiver on the horizon, spread
By celestial palette knife,
Encrusted still with starlight, and
Blanching sea to pale cyan
A million flares—like comet brine
Crystal fire in my eyes
Dancing sprites with diamond chimes
Skywater burning bright.

I roll with the deeper gong and flow,
Sway in the seaweed garden,
Summon the swirling train of foam,
And don my silvery garment.
This is a day to rise and sing,
To leap and kiss the sun.

# BLUE TIT

## BY SHIRALEE MATTHEWS

QUICK flit blue tit
  Head tilt, beak dip,
  Wing flip, gone.

# CAMILLE AND THE BRITISH ADVENTURE

## (THE BALLAD OF PETTICOAT LANE)
## BY DON MUNNINGS

TO THE land of roast beef, our French hero embarked,
  with manservant Igor in tow.
At the Palace Hotel, they were comf'tably parked,
A very posh gaff, don't-you-know?

Their fame, it had spread like trees in a wood,
or waste oil in a puddle of rain.
The request was to travel as soon as they could,
and book seats on a London-bound train.

Camille informed Igor, "We've just had the call,"
as he put the phone down on its stand.
They gathered their coats as they passed through the hall,
then toddled away up the Strand.

"The British are strange and incredibly mad,"
Camille was then forced to remark,
as a fellow barged past like a lowly born cad,
and probably thought it a lark.

31

The day promised rain with a sprinkling of mud,
as the pair of them skipped to the kerb.
Hailing a taxi without loss of blood,
their footwork was really superb.

Instructions to drive to a club at St James,
were issued in strangled Franglaise.
The cabby complained he had not understood,
and drove there by roundabout ways.

The doorman jumped to at the sight of Camille,
with his posture so noble and grand,
as he justly rewarded the man at the wheel,
by pressing a crown in his hand.

They were hailed by Sir Arnold, a splendid old cove,
bewigged and bewhiskered and large.
The three of them settled in seats by the stove,
to talk of their task, and the charge.

Any fee they might ask he would not give a hang,
to save his sweet daughter from shame,
and rescue the lass from a cockerney gang,
but first he must give them her name.

"My daughter's called Florence, aged just twenty-one,
eyes of blue and with burnished gold hair.
She hasn't been seen for a couple of weeks.
I'm concerned, and my wife's in despair.

"My Flo must be saved from becoming depraved,
by Flash 'Arry—the cockney seducer.
The poor girl can't see she's becoming enslaved,
so, for help, I am turning to you, sah."

A deal it was done, Arnold gave them a gun,
and twelve guineas to cover expenses.
Saying, "Meeting Flash 'Arry will never be fun,
take care, and don't drop your defences."

In their suite in the Strand, with money in hand,
well replete with their champagne and lobsters,
they agreed it was better to not show their hand,
in pursuit of these cockerney mobsters.

"We'll assume a disguise, mingle in with the crowd,"
Camille reasoned after long thought.
"Dress as typical cockneys, though in no way loud."
So, two pearly suits were then bought.

They rode a steam tramcar to Petticoat Lane,
where cockneys were known to disport.
Their apparel was greeted with mirthful disdain,
so their stay at the venue was short.

Camille was downcast, his companion aghast,
at their foolish sartorial gaffe.
He reasoned they'd always won through in the past,
if they failed, they'd at least have a laugh.

"There is work to be done, and discretion's the key,
in pursuit of this bad cockney sparrer.
Costermongers look neat and abound on the street.
Go to Bow, and there purchase a 'barrer.'"

So they went back again, dahn Petticoat lane,
equipped with a barrer-boy's cart.
Decked with whelks and fine winkles artistically lain,
and feeling quite smug with their art.

They asked a small urchin to "Give 'em the goods."
on where 'Arry's gang would be found.
He confessed he'd feel bad at betraying the hoods,
but not if they gave him a crown.

At around about five in an Eel and Pie dive,
some cockneys woofed down jellied eel.
Some folks had tried them, and barely survived,
and thought that the taste was unreal.

33

'Arry played on the spoons and sang a love song,
as sweet Florence near swooned with affection.
From their place of concealment our heroes looked on,
much doubting she'd need their protection.

Camille then leapt out with a thunderous shout,
"Unhand her, you rascal," he called.
'Arry said, "Blimey! Oi lads! Sling 'im out...
and then string him up by his balls."

Before this could be done, Igor pulled out the gun,
And joyfully joined the affray.
He said, "You can be shot but I'd rather you run,
you'd be safer much further away."

With consummate care, grabbing Flo by her hair,
Camille stuffed the sweet girl in a sack.
He informed her her daddy was close to despair,
then in triumph they dragged their prize back.

Flo in no way contrite in her daddy's stern sight,
as he waved an admonishing finger,
Said, "Got engaged to my Harry last Saturday night.
In your house I would rather not linger.

"I've been put in the club: in the 'rub-a-dub-dub',
put that in your pipe, and then smoke it.
I've reached twenty-one, the deed has been done,
I don't want a dowry—so poke it."

In spite of the outcome, Camille claimed his fee,
He was paid without having to grovel.
Sir Arnold cast Florence back out on the street,
to raise 'Arry's kids in an 'ovel.

As they steamed through the night, England fading from sight,
Camille then expounded the moral:
Consort with a cockney who eats jellied eels,
then you and your daddy may quarrel.

# Caught Blue Handed

## By Lee Stoddart

THE roadster sat gleaming in the warm sun. With her soft-top roof stowed away, she looked like a shark basking in the driveway. Built in the same year as me. A forty-eight-year-old classic, still sleek and dangerous. Her polar paintwork transformed from a cold-grey in shadow, to a shimmering silver-blue as the sunlight flashed across her bonnet.

The full-leather interior was a dark navy.

Or rather, it should have been. Over the years, the sun had bleached the colour from the cracked-leather seats and dashboard and faded them to the dark, off-green of the sea on a stormy day.

I tried to keep it in top shape and did as much as I could myself. I even had my own pit in the garage, so I could work on the engine and underbody, although I hadn't been able to use it for a while because it was fully utilised storing some old shit I really should have dumped by now. Some jobs just get away from us, don't they?

There was no doubting it though, she was in superb shape. Worth a tidy sum, too. Not many 280 SLs out there in her condition. So, the less-than-perfect state of the inside really irked me and I'd decided it was high-time to do something about it. All morning, I'd been attacking the seats with a leather colour restorer, very much like shoe polish except it was gloopier, less of a hard wax. Its light chemical perfume pervaded the air as it dried on both the seating and my hands. I'd forgotten to put protective gloves on, *again*, and the gunk had stained me as happily as it stained the interior of the car.

"Oh, shit. It's on my tee-shirt, too." My new, white tee, ruined. The black outline cartoon-image of *Futurama's* Dr Zoidberg dressed as that guy from *Breaking Bad*, smeared with a blue streak running across his tentacled face and pork pie hat. My daughter had bought it for me as a birthday present just a few weeks ago. She was going to be pissed at me. Love her as I do, she can be a pain in the arse when she's got the hump.

"Like I need that," I muttered.

"Like you need what?"

35

I turned. Tabatha had snuck up behind me whilst my head was down in the car. She was fifteen years my junior and, at thirty-three, she carried her years lightly, whereas I was beginning to settle into the comfortable spread of middle age despite her efforts to keep me trim.

I extended my arms, sticky blue hands high above my head then zeroed down to point at the offending stain.

"Oh, that. Boy, you *are* in trouble." She wagged her finger and smirked, even as she said it.

I lunged at her, playfully making out to smear her yellow summer top across her boobs, but she stepped back and deftly evaded my clumsy efforts.

"Lucky for you, Rhianna isn't about." I must have looked quizzically at her. "She's up the road, playing with her friends on their bikes," she elucidated. "Why don't you strip that shirt off and I'll see if I can get it washed out before she sees it, whilst you finish off here? I've got some of that pink stuff somewhere…"

She gave me a look that said 'you wouldn't dare', and then reached out and took hold of the bottom of my shirt, indicating with an upward nod that I should raise my arms again. I allowed her to lift it over my head, my arms stretched high so that she had to reach up to her full extent on tip-toes, pushing her hips and chest forward.

"I'm quite partial to *your* pink stuff…" I sleazed. There were advantages to being off the main road, including a big, secluded private drive down the side of the house, know what I mean?

"Steady, tiger. She'll be home soon, and I've got no time for your hankie-pankie, Roger Malkovich. Besides, you better hurry up and finish the car off, it looks like rain."

She was right, but I gave her my best puppy-dog eyes anyway and she relented enough to sidle close in as she clutched the obviously ruined shirt protectively to her chest.

"Guess I'd better order another," I said. "That stuff's designed not to come out once it's dry. You'll never wash it out. Do you know where she got it from?"

"Roger, honestly. Your daughter's eight." *Your* daughter, not *our* daughter. Rhianna had never *quite* taken to her new mum, always a daddy's girl. "Who do you think bought it? Might as well go for an extra X as well, this one looks like it was a bit... snug. I'll get onto Amazon."

I grunted, not wanting to admit I might be needing an XL rather than my usual L. I planted a kiss on her lips and she responded just enough to get me interested before she unwound herself from my arms and spiralled away, giggling.

"Tease," I called after her, laughingly, unable to tear my eyes from her playfully exaggerated, gyrating derrière.

I suppose I couldn't really blame her.

When Tabatha pulled that t-shirt up I could feel my belly drop forward a little until it hung ever so slightly over my belt. Age was catching up on me but she was still in her prime. She'd never had kids to worry about ruining her perfect figure.

And, I ask you, why wouldn't she stray?

I kind of always thought there was a chance she might, right from day one.

If she'd let herself go, and started spreading, *I'd* be looking for a new model, no question. You'd do the same, right? Why should I expect her to act any different?

How did we come together?

Well, you can laugh, but it was a total cliché; classic secretary snags boss when he's on the rebound. We were working long hours together and I was going through the whole divorce thing with Sandra, my whore-wife at the time, before she unexpectedly took off, not to be seen again.

That's not to say I wasn't grateful for Tab's attention. A celebration dinner after we nailed a particularly large contract quickly turned into a regular event, then bed. When, late one evening, we were caught in the office by the cleaner, 'in flagrante delicto', we both had to leave the business. It wasn't 'appropriate'.

To be honest, that couldn't have worked out better if I'd planned it. I'd been a director at McKinnon's Asset & Wealth Management long enough to know where *all* the skeletons were buried. I left with a tidy compromise agreement, enough to ensure I didn't have to worry about work again before my rather generous pension kicked in. And it was quite convenient that Sandra disappeared before she had a chance to take me to the cleaners in a big divorce, no doubt with a hoard of money-grabbing solicitors in tow.

At least with the old cow out the way, it meant Tabs could move in. That was nearly two years ago.

Anyway, despite all my experience with contracts, I'd never quite got around to writing any kind of prenup, not that we were married. What do they call them? A cohabitation agreement? I simply hadn't expected it to last long enough for it to matter. I suppose I couldn't believe my luck. She was beautiful, smart and funny. She ran my life for me, like she was still my PA. With *benefits*.

Then, one night in our local pub, just after we'd been caught red-handed in the office, I confided in George, my best pal—he was like the younger brother I'd never had, and he supported me right from the off. I asked him whether I should let her move in and what would my mates think?

"They'd think 'lucky bastard'. That's what they'd think," he'd said, grinning.

"Sure, but what would they *say*? That I was robbing the cradle?" I challenged.

"Honestly, mate," he replied, "Who gives a fuck what they say *or* think when you've got *her* waiting at home? I'd do her in a moment. Bollocks to 'em."

I always listened to George; a bit 'new-lad', liked to play the field, but I valued his opinion, especially when I agreed with him. Even with a bit of hindsight, he seemed a bit too keen on Tabatha.

Move forward a year, and I found myself back in the Frog and Calculator, confiding in George again, a few pints worse-for-wear.

"I'm worried mate, it's been nearly twelve-months since she moved in. She must have *rights* by now, hasn't she? Rights to the house, my pension, *the car*... and now, it feels too long to go back and demand an agreement. It wasn't supposed to last even this long." As I told him, it was just meant to be a bit of fun, you know?

Ever the pragmatist, George responded. "Do you love her, or is it just lust? Would you care if she upped and left?"

"Sure, I would. And it's love, I guess. Maybe. Oh, I don't know. Lust. Whatever. But, she's going to get bored with this old fart soon enough, isn't she? She's still young..."

"So, marry her. Lock her in."

"Really? But that gives her even more rights doesn't it? If she's just a gold-digger, I might... *Rhianna* might lose the lot, if I snuff it."

Besides, Sandra was still missing and the divorce petition hadn't been served because the court couldn't find her, which was a right royal pain in the arse, I can tell you.

"You could still get engaged. Shows intent... without any real commitment. Pending the divorce coming through, or you getting bored..."

"Yeah, maybe."

Pause. "There's only one thing you can do..." He left a second, longer pause. Perfect timing is one of George's strong points. "You'll have to kill her. That's all there is to it."

I looked at him incredulously, and then we both burst out laughing before taking another huge gulp of our pints.

* * * * *

"Treacherous, fucking bastard!"

It wasn't more than a month or two after we'd been in the pub that second time. I'd agreed, against my better judgement, to do a spot of consultancy for a friend who was setting up a new business in Manchester. All a bit dodgy, given the non-compete clauses in my exit contract from McKinnon, but it was cash-in-hand and *very* lucrative. Exactly the kind of thing I needed to top up the coffers and keep my hand in the game.

I'd been away for a couple of nights. It had been good to see Andrew. We'd spent the days working hard and the evenings playing harder. On the last day, we'd finished a little quicker than expected, so I caught an earlier train, intending to take the girls out to make up for me being away.

As the taxi swung into the driveway, I could hardly miss the red Porsche parked across my garage. I'd always told him that it wasn't subtle. Not like my Merc. Too noticeable, too 'in your face'. The number plate didn't help either: G304 GEP spaced out as G304GE P. Vulgar little shit.

I should have known. Now I look back, I can see all those coy little looks.

What did he say? 'I'd do her in a moment.' Fucker.

I threw a twenty at the driver and told him to keep the change, dragged my case out of the car and left it lying in a puddle on the gravel. Fumbling for my keys I ran to the door and stabbed them at the lock, desperate to get the door open. I'd catch the pair of them at it.

As I repeatedly missed the keyhole, I heard feet running up on the other side of the door. Suddenly, the handle lurched down and the door was thrown open. I was ready to defend myself from his inevitable assault when, rather than confronting George, Rhianna threw herself into my arms, her chubby face beaming.

"Daddeeee—you're home early! Uncle George is here. He's going to take me to ballet tonight in his *PORSCHE* because Tabbie's car is 'a piece of old crap and broken... *again*'." She emphasised the 'again' exactly how Tabatha would have, all exasperation and despair. "Perhaps you should buy Tabbie a nice red sports car so we don't have to rely on Uncle George all the time."

As she spoke, George emerged from the lounge into the hall, Tabatha trailing him.

"What—" I ejaculated, but George interrupted.

"Sorry, maaate. I popped around to see you, to ask your advice on something. Forgot you weren't about. Anyway, seems Tabbie's old Evoke has thrown its toys out the pram, and I was just hanging on to give Rhianna a lift to her class in the *Turbo*." I'd never noticed before, but he sounds just like Jeremy Clarkson sometimes. Crass twat.

"It's *much* faster than your old blue thing, daddy."

"Hmmm... Yes, well, it's much *newer*. And speed isn't everything..." Besides, the Merc was worth more.

He'd completely wrong-footed me with his little speech. He damn well knew I was off for a few days. "Couldn't you have just got a taxi?" I stared accusingly at Tabatha.

"Oh, but dear, George offered, and Rhianna was so excited to go out in the Porsche. She's really a little bit of a speed-freak, I think." She's all smiles. Nothing wrong in the world. *Conniving, duplicitous whore.*

"Well, you're home now, Roger. I can get out of your way— I'm sure you'll want to *say hello* properly." George picked up his keys from the console table in the hall.

40

"Oh, but Uncle George…" Rhianna wailed.

"Maybe another time, Rhianna. Your dad's home now… unless he *wants* me to take you?"

*Nice. Keep up the pretence. Arsehole.*

"No, that's fine. *Thanks*, George. I'll take it from here." I stepped out of his way and let him slip past into the driveway. He climbed into the car and fired it up with the unruliest roar—it was no stealth car designed for clandestine assignations, to be sure.

Before he'd left the drive, I'd closed the door behind me. Tabatha seemed to be craning her beautiful, long neck to see the last of him off; but maybe I imagined it.

"Right, who wants pizza?" I suggested.

"Pizza, pizza, PIZZA!" Rhianna bounced up and down, grinning like a loon. Pizza had been a no-no since Tabatha came on the scene. She said it was too dangerous for her figure and constant take-aways weren't doing the child any good, let alone me.

"But Rhianna's got classes," Tabatha unsubtly reminded me, as if I didn't know.

"And your car's broken, so she can't get there."

"There's always a taxi, or the Merc."

"You know the Merc's not a run-around."

"Pizzzzzaaaaa!" Rhianna yelled, full volume.

"Pizza it is then," Tabatha capitulated. "Anything for a quiet life."

That night, with Rhianna in bed, complaining of stomach-ache after too much pizza, ice cream and coke, Tabatha and I had our first *really* significant row.

I downed a couple of stiff whiskies whilst I accused her of flirting with George—she *knew* what a player he was, and he's just that bit younger than me and a bit fitter. No kids hanging about. Flash car. Everything she'd want in an *upgrade*. I stopped just short of accusing her of sleeping with him. I guess there was a tiny corner of my mind that didn't want to believe it and maybe, just maybe, she hadn't.

It was like I was talking to Sandra all over again. Tabatha was all denials and recriminations—demanding to know what I'd been doing in Manchester with Andrew. She knew full-well what a muff-hound the old bugger was, from when she was my PA. He'd even

41

tried it on with her once or twice—although, she always insisted, *unsuccessfully*. She actually managed to name two of the clubs we'd gone back to visit for old time's sake, from old expense claims she'd processed. Both notorious strip joints. And when I say strip joints, I mean knocking shops.

Then it was drink-fuelled anger from me and tears from her as she stormed off to bed in the spare room whilst I finished the bottle.

The next morning, when I walked bleary-eyed into the kitchen, it was to find a note propped up against the teapot:

'Roger,

I can't take any more of your jealousy bullshit. Every time someone even passes me a compliment, you get all aggressive and throw your weight around. Yesterday, with George, was the last straw. He's your best friend, for God's sake. Give Rhianna my love, I shall miss her.

Tabatha'

A single star-shaped splash had made a pale blue halo in the ink, highlighting the middle of 'aggressive'.

"What the hell's she going on about?" Given the circumstances, I thought I had behaved like the *perfect* gentleman. Something would have to be done. No one walks out on *me*.

Fortunately, it was Rhianna's turn to get picked up for school by her best friend's mum. I don't think there was any way I should be driving—I was still pissed.

Jasmine, I noticed, had a real 'yummy mummy'. You know the type? Legs way up to *here* as she climbed out her brand-new Range Rover Sport, top boob-job (no way *those* were real). I'd heard from Tabatha that her marriage was on the rocks six months ago. Maybe I should've helped her get over the trauma.

Rhianna grimaced at me as she slunk past, her eyes red-raw with blubbing. I guess she was still suffering from stuffing her fat, little face the previous night. Jasmine's mum ushered Rhianna into the back seat of the car, scowling at me all the while, before roaring off.

*What the hell's got her all riled-up?* I thought. But, who can tell with girls, eh? Almost as trying as when they grow up.

With the kid out of the way, I'd intended to spend the rest of the morning finishing off the interior on the Merc, to distract myself from Tabatha's little spat. She'd inevitably repent and find her way back, then there'd be the make-up sex. After that, I planned to tell her she was dumped. But, saddled with the mother of all hangovers, I instead spent the next few hours nursing my head on the sofa, accompanied by some 'hair of the dog', and didn't get to the car until mid-afternoon.

Eventually, I dragged myself out to the garage. It always made me smile to see her sitting there. In the harsh glare of the triple garage's neon strip-lighting, she really shone. But, as I bent to unlock the car door, I noticed the deep gouge in her perfect paintwork. A jagged white line scored down to the metal, from one end of the car to the other. I followed it as it circumnavigated the boot and continued its journey up the passenger side, across the bonnet, to re-join itself, like the world-serpent biting its own tail.

"Oh, no. No, no, no…" my litany of denial echoed around the garage. I stood there, staring at the ruined bodywork, clenching and unclenching my fists. "No fucking way!"

I threw the driver's door open and inelegantly wedged myself behind the wheel. Maybe it wouldn't look so bad in the sunshine, but, even then, I knew it was a forlorn hope. The original paintwork was destroyed forever.

As my arse hit the seat cushion, I felt an unpleasant squishy sensation, like I'd just sat in a pile of shit. Simultaneously, my foot kicked something hollow and plastic on the floor. My only thought was to get the car out in the open air, to inspect every inch, in the sunlight. I turned the key and knocked the car into gear. I put my foot on the gas too hard and my heel slipped on the goo that covered the floor, compressing the accelerator further still. The Mercedes inline-6 roared as I over-revved her, and the car screeched forward.

Too distracted to respond, the car rocketed forward. I desperately hit the brakes, but the near-empty pot of leather treatment had skittered under the pedal, propelled there by my errant foot, and we continued our journey out of the garage virtually unabated until we collided with the ancient oak tree on the other side of the drive.

The bonnet crumpled and, unseatbelted, I continued my journey forward, smashing my head against the windscreen.

Vision blurred, I lifted myself off the steering wheel and strained to suck in air—my chest hurt like hell as I sat slumped in the seat. You know how it is? I thought I was having a heart attack, but I was just bruised from the impact on the steering wheel. I lifted my hand to an enormous, throbbing lump on my head. Sticky fingers came away navy-blue, with traces of red on the tips.

Panicking a little, my slippery digits pulled ineffectively at the door handle until it finally sprang open, and I half-fell, half-slithered out of the wreck of my beautiful car, my formerly near-perfect pride and joy.

In the sunlight I could see the interior had been liberally coated in great dollops of the navy-blue leather treatment, smooshed in where I'd sat on it and spread it about. But, no amount of dye could camouflage the deep scissor-cuts in the leather.

"Bitch... she's gonna get what she deserves."

Rhianna was watching me from the end of the driveway where Jasmine's mum had dropped her and driven off without coming in. The kid looked like she was in shock, taking tentative steps towards me, sobbing.

"Oh, Daddy. I—"

To my amazement, I didn't fly off the handle at her. "Be quiet and go inside. I'll be back later," was all I said.

Bawling, she hesitated until I took a step towards her, then she shot past me and disappeared into the house. I could still see her peeking through the letter box, until I stared hard at the eyes looking out. Slowly, the flap descended. She'd got the message.

With Rhianna out the way, I went back into the garage, grabbed a crowbar from the toolbox and used it to pry the front bumper out into a serviceable shape, then threw the metal rod onto the passenger seat. The driver's side front-wheel arch needed a few hearty tugs to get it off the wheel.

I gave her a quick once over, jumped into the driver's seat, turned the engine over and threw her into reverse. With the wheel on full lock the wing still ground on the wheel making one hell of a racket, and the rad was properly knackered, dripping coolant across the drive, but I didn't care. I was off, flying up the road and heading for George's.

George's place had an in-out drive that, if it's possible, was even more impressive than mine; the joy of not having any hangers-on to weigh your bank balance down, I suppose.

I swung into it fast, wheel squealing then gravel flying everywhere as I hit the brakes. Sitting in front of the house, bold as brass, was her bloody Evoke and his in-your-face red fucking Turbo.

Before I could think, I was out the Merc, crowbar in hand.

Smash... one new windscreen required.

Smash, smash... two new headlights.

Smash, smash, smash... bonnet dented like he'd hit a deer.

*Ha, ha! Bet they're not cheap on a fucking Porsche.*

I stood breathless in front of the car, yelling at the house. "Where are the pair of you? Come on, let's have it out, right here and now!"

A few moments passed, pregnant with suspense, before the heavy, oak, front door opened and George emerged. Tabatha cowered behind him. She looked like she'd been crying and clutched a wodge of tissues in her hand. In *his* hands he cradled a double-barrelled shotgun he used for clay shooting. Uncowed I strode up to them, intent on a confrontation.

"What the fuck, Roger? My car!" he yelled as I approached, the barrel lowering towards me. "You've gone too far this time. You drove Sandra out and now you've done the same with Tabatha. She's distraught and just wants to get away from you."

I couldn't stand any more of his lies. "How dare you... you're supposed to be my best mate. How long have you been fucking her, George? And *you*, why the hell take it out on *my* car? Bitch!"

Tabatha looked back at me blankly, feigning she didn't know what I was talking about. George looked confused. Quite the pair of innocents.

"I've never touched her, Rog. We're mates, I wouldn't do that—"

"Don't lie to me!" I thrust the crowbar at him, angrily waving it about like an extension of an angry, wagging finger. Slick with greasy blue dye, it slipped out of my hand at the end of one particularly forceful gesticulation. It flew towards George, chisel

45

edge first, hitting him square in the eye. He keeled backwards, shotgun raised. His head struck the front step with a resounding crack. Traumatised from the shock of my unintended assault, I stood motionless. Tabatha screamed and knelt beside him, cradling his broken skull, blood oozing over her hands as his right foot twitched.

Suddenly, George convulsed, finger still on the trigger.

The shotgun fired in a great crack as he gave one final spasm. Tabatha looked down at her stomach, bemused. In disbelief, she dipped her finger into the oozing, charred-edge, crimson hole in her stomach. Blood soaked her white sweater, spread rapidly across her chest. She looked up at me one last time, like I might be able to save her, then collapsed across George's body.

I think I was in shock, standing there, rubbernecking like it was a traffic accident—mute and untouchable. I must have been in shock from witnessing such a horrible accident. Then, it was as though I had been thrown back into my body. My gorge rose and I threw up bile onto the gravel.

* * * * *

"So, that's my story, doc. The sad tale of how I ended up here, in Broadmoor, just under six months ago. Betrayed by the woman I loved and my best friend. The bitch even turned my daughter against me.

"A total miscarriage of justice. I never meant either of them to die. An accident. Still, my trial's coming up. You'll support me, eh?"

The interview room is the same cold, blue-grey the SL went in shadow, his cheap suit the same navy as the car's interior. I can do without the reminder, to be frank.

I *really* miss that car.

"I'm sorry, Roger. I think you misunderstand my role. I'm not here to support you. I'm just here to report my findings to the court. Objectively. And, I find your account of events extraordinary when compared to the evidence."

"Really? Not sure what you mean."

"The CCTV at the house clearly shows you swinging the crowbar at Mr Lawrence, killing him with a deliberate, single blow. You then grabbed the gun and shot Miss Osmund point blank in the gut, fatally wounding her, leaving her to bleed out. Then, you completely omit how you returned home and... well, I can barely bring myself to say what you did to your daughter."

The shrink shakes his head and breathes out heavily, as though freeing himself of an unpleasant image.

"That's not true. I never touched the gun. Why are you making this stuff up? Jesus, everyone's against me," I tell him.

"Then why did the stock have traces of the same blue dye your car was covered in? The same blue dye that, weeks on, still darkens your hands?" He looks down at the table between us.

I unclasp my hands. I hadn't realised I was wringing them. And he doesn't need to remind me about the stain. I'd washed them as often as the awful regime in here allowed, but, months after, I still can't get the discolouration out.

*Out damned spot! Out I say!*

"I... don't know. The police must have set me up."

"Why? Why would they do that, Roger?"

"Who cares? To meet their conviction targets? It was an accident."

"And, what about your daughter—"

"We were gonna skip the country; but, she wouldn't come with me. So, I sent her off to be with her mum."

"You certainly did."

"There you are then. She might be only eight, but she can tell you what was going on. *If* you can find the pair of them."

"Roger, the police *did* find her—you *know* that.

"Brutalised, in the pit under *your* garage floor, because she took her frustration and anger out on your car. She was screaming her head off because you left her down there on top of the rotting corpse of her mother; whilst you polished the wreck of your fucking Mercedes parked over the top of them."

He gets up and walks to the door, banging on it to be allowed out. Before he goes, he turns to face me once more. "Roger... I wouldn't plan on going out for a drive for a very long time."

47

# CHILDHOOD SUMMER

## BY SHIRALEE MATTHEWS

BLUE haze headache
Sunshine-tight skin
Drowsy ride home

# CLEANING THE PAST

## BY SHIRALEE MATTHEWS

MONDAY
Returning to your childhood home is always difficult, especially if you've been estranged from your parents for thirty years. This is, of course, compounded by their sudden and unexpected deaths. It seems that, despite losing his licence, my father insisted on driving to the supermarket for the weekly shop.

I'm standing at the gate of what was a well-set-up Edwardian villa, trying to find the courage to go in. The front garden is overgrown, with hedges as high as the first floor. *I'll have to get a professional in to sort that out, I can't do it myself.* Setting my shoulders, I get out the keys and walk to the front door. The stained-glass image of a boat at sea is still there along with the lion's head knocker.

Opening the front door is easy and the electricity is still turned on but the smell that rolls out is overwhelming, an indefinable mixture of old age, lavender and dirt. I wait for nose-blindness to set in but it's taking its time. Taking a deep breath, I scuttle my way to the back door. This is more difficult to open and I wonder if I'll do it before I throw up.

Agitation slows me but finally the key turns and I stumble out into the fresh air, gulping in new breath. I sit in the even more overgrown back garden, giving the house a chance to breathe, making a to-do list and arranging a skip—anything to avoid going back in. When I do, all I can see is the dirt and grease; the kitchen hasn't been cleaned for years. Shopping is my next priority.

My mobile rings as I'm unloading the car. "How are you doing, love?"

"Not bad, but it's worse than I thought it would be."

"Do you want me to come?"

"No, I need to do this myself. I've extended the hotel till the end of the week."

"Okay. The kids send their love. They're dying to see the place."

"I promise you'll all get the tour when it's fit for humans."

"Call me if you need anything."

"Thanks, love to you all."

I've bought enough cleaning stuff to scrub the Forth Bridge—creams, sprays, bleaches, rubber gloves, micro-cloths, brushes, a broom, rubbish bags—a whole shopping trolley full. Sitting on the kitchen table, they are the cleanest things in the house.

I start with the downstairs toilet—I'd rather pee in the garden than use it in its current state. Even though it's the smallest room, it still takes the rest of the day. One room, clean and sweet smelling with an odour neutraliser sitting on the window shelf.

Before I finish for the day, I walk through the house leaving odour neutralisers in every room. My parents' room, musty with dirty clothes and bedding; my old bedroom, stripped back to its bare bones, cold and anonymous. The two guest bedrooms are equally dusty and empty. The two bathrooms, one for my mother and one for my father, both littered with detritus—toothpaste smears in the basins and rings around the baths.

The music room, with the piano that I learned to play on, still has a side table piled with sheet music and old magazines. The drawing room is a surprise. When I was a child, this was where guests were entertained. It had the best furniture and the most tasteful decorations. Now it is stuffed full of knick-knacks, broken furniture and torn fabrics. There's enough room to circumvent the main pieces but there are just too many things. The table in the dining room is piled high with crockery—a random collection of mis-matched pieces, some broken, all covered in dust. As I walk through these rooms I feel the lack of care and it saddens me. In the living room there is mouldy food on plates next to the sofa and a smell of stale beer. And the kitchen. I hate the kitchen. I hated it when I was a child and I hate it now. It is by far the worst room, the grease of countless fried dinners magnetically attracting dust and dirt in a thick layer. Every surface is sticky and I cringe at the thought of the work needed.

**Tuesday**
Today is kitchen day. The smell hasn't diminished much but I can keep the back door open so it isn't as bad as before. Sweeping the ceiling brings down a halo of cobwebs and washing the walls takes a good couple of hours. I hate cleaning but I'm good at it. It was the only job I could get when I left my parents' house. The rhythms come back and my mind starts to wander, remembering my childhood. Every evening after dinner it was my job to wash the dishes, wipe them up and put them away. My mother always said she had enough to do cooking for us and needed her rest.

Tuesday night was bin night which often delayed me as I had to empty the wastepaper baskets from all the rooms before taking the rubbish outside. But I was quick and thorough, usually managing to finish before my father came in to inspect the kitchen. No 'Thank you', but 'Upstairs and do your homework, don't go disturbing us.' To be honest it was a relief to get away from them. I didn't know that not everyone lived like that, I assumed everyone did chores and then went to their bedroom. My two girls do their chores, but we thank them and spend time with them. I have Jack to thank for that. I wasn't going to set chores, but he said it would be good for them and a learning experience. It would bond the family, and it would give them some skills and a sense of responsibility—he can go on, but he's a good man and a good father.

Next, I tackle the windows. We used to have a man who did them, but I doubt my parents even noticed when he stopped coming. It's amazing how much light comes into the kitchen considering the overgrown back garden, and how much brighter the room seems. I remember daydreaming during my Saturday chores, making up music to fit the movement of the trees and the sounds of the birds. The kitchen table is wooden so in need of a good scrub, top and legs. When I was a child it was too heavy for me to lift but now I can shift it, one side at a time. It leaves deep indentations in the lino—the vivid blue of the original pattern leaps out at me and I wonder if I'll ever be able to bring the rest of the floor up to that colour.

Once the table's been scrubbed and is no longer sticky, I take my lunch out to the garden, glad to relax for a while. It's a sunny day and I try to remember if I ever played out here. I never brought friends home. To be honest I didn't really have any. I sit on a stone bench, eating and thinking about the last day I spent in the garden. A feeling of sadness wraps around me and I feel cold. No, I don't have time for self-pity—there's a fridge and freezer to be cleaned.

The freezer is almost empty and totally iced-up so I leave that to defrost while I tackle the fridge. The food is mouldy—thank god for rubbish bags—and all of it is processed garbage, either waiting to be deep fried or baked in the oven. I'm surprised my parents didn't buy a microwave but maybe that was just too much new technology for them. While I'm waiting for the freezer I scrub the sink and the cooker. I've bought that ecologically unfriendly oven cleaner to deal with the years of grease. I shouldn't be surprised that my mother couldn't see how filthy the cooker had become. She didn't have to do it while I was there though she was quick enough to snap, 'All you need is washing up liquid and elbow grease!' Which is easy to say when you don't have to do it. I'll never bring the cooker up to it's original look but it's clean and mostly stain-free by time I've finished.

My shoulders are beginning to ache, bringing back memories of past Saturday evenings, but the freezer is now clean and all that is left is the floor. It's tempting to try the modern floor cleaners but I doubt they're strong enough. I want this floor to shine like the last time I cleaned it so I'm on my knees with a scrubbing brush and hot water. There is something very satisfying about seeing the colour of the floor change. From grimy grey to a pale blue, not the brilliance of the original colour—I will have to move the table back into the indentations—but lighter and friendlier than before. As I sit back on my heels I realise that it isn't sweat running down my face but tears. All those years, all that stubbornness. Had anyone even cleaned the floor in the last thirty years? Had my mother avoided it in the belief that I would be coming back, or was it left as a punishment?

## Wednesday

I feel a little paralysed and unwilling to face the tasks ahead. I should deal with the living room, but I don't want to. I compromise and clean the dining room. It's obvious that it hasn't been used for many years and mostly I have to sort out crockery—broken from unbroken. In the sideboard I find our everyday dining set. The set I had to wash up every night. Plain white with no embellishment, it's like an old friend and I wash it so I can use it again. The rest I'll donate or dispose of. We have plenty of crockery at home and this cracked, glazed ware is nothing special. Most of it must have been bought after I left, god knows why. Still avoiding the living room, I tackle the drawing room. By the time I've emptied the two rooms of rubbish, the skip is half full. I am proud that I've rescued the rooms from my parents. I feel a vicious joy, almost a v-sign to them—I've saved these rooms from you as I saved myself from you.

I finish by lunchtime and decide to deal with the music room. Again, this room doesn't seem to have been used much. The piano is out of tune and the dust is stifling. This room was where I escaped on Sundays. A quick dust and tidy and I was free to play. I can hear my father's voice, 'Practice makes perfect.' And, 'We didn't spend all that money on lessons for you to slack off.' Of all the things my parents did, this is the one thing I'm grateful for. Music has sustained me over the last three decades, bringing me joy and love. I google 'piano tuner' and arrange for someone to come over on Friday. My piano is beautiful and I hope it can be saved. I want to be able to sit down and play it again. Despite everything, I want my parents to know the money wasn't wasted. I sort out the sheet music and throw away the magazines. The curtains fall apart as I try to take them down and the windows are filthy but I'm in the mood for vinegar and newspapers. A couple of hours later the room is shining and I'm smiling.

I phone Jack that evening. "Is everything ok? Do the kids miss me? Do you miss me?" I'm feeling very needy, and he reassures me.

"We're coping fine, the kids want to know when you're coming home, and I can't sleep properly without you." I feel a warmth wrap around me at his voice.

"I love you, husband of mine. Have an early night and dream about me." I can hear his smile as he says goodnight.

## Thursday

I'm still avoiding the living room. I've decided to leave it to last, to wipe out all the other memories.

I'm told that most people find clearing their deceased parents' bedroom is the most difficult thing to do. I lost my parents when I was sixteen. Their bedroom is a foreign land to me—it was the one room I was never allowed into. Looking at it now, I can't see what there was to hide. I open the windows, take down the disintegrating curtains and bin them. I strip the bed, nothing worth keeping, and start on the wardrobes.

My parents' clothes are fusty and old-fashioned. I can't imagine anyone wanting them and, to be honest, I get a quiet joy from filling rubbish bags and throwing them in the skip. The same for the chest of drawers. I don't bother going through pockets, there would be nothing I want. My mother's jewellery I put in a plastic box for my daughters to sort through and my father's bits and bobs can go to my son—if he wants them.

After lunch I move onto the bathrooms, grubby but not difficult to clean. I throw away the accumulated toiletries, leaving both the rooms and me empty. As the day goes on I find I'm concentrating solely on cleaning and avoiding my memories. I know tomorrow will be difficult but when it's done I will truly be free.

That night I call Dan.

"Hello Dan, it's your mum."

"How are you doing? Has it been difficult?"

"Funnily enough, it's got better as the week's gone on. I should be finished tomorrow, and I wondered if you and Nicky would like to come down for the day on Saturday and see the place. You could bring the baby. Jack and the girls will be here, and we could have a picnic."

"I'd like to see the place. What time would be good?"
"Ten-ish?"

## Friday

The piano tuner is due today and I can't let him see the living room. It seems some values have been passed on and I need that push to help me tackle it.

How many hours of their lives did they spend in this room? I'm trying to imagine them burrowing into their chairs, watching television and it just doesn't resonate. Who were these old people? How could they live in such disarray? Should I have made more effort?

Despite the odour neutraliser, the smell is unpleasant. As usual I start by opening the windows—thank god I've had good weather this week—and tearing down the curtains. Those and the disintegrating cushions go into rubbish bags. The mouldy food (and the plates it's on) go straight into another rubbish bag. Once the obvious debris is removed, I start at the top, sweeping the ceiling (sorry spiders), cleaning windows and dusting furniture. So much tat to be thrown away, so many magazines to be recycled; how much detritus can one couple accumulate? Did they start buying to avoid the gap I left? Did it make them feel better or were they compensating themselves for my ingratitude? As I brush and polish, dust and vacuum I start sobbing. Furious at their cruelty and my loss. This is probably the room my parents used the most but I have no sense of them here.

This is the room that I dreaded. This is where I told them I was pregnant and where they told me to leave.

# CLEAR BLUE WATERS

## BY LEE STODDART

*(First published in Blue Nib, 1ˢᵗ August 2020; due for publication in the Paris-based Menteur Magazine, June 2021)*

A SOLITARY bubble floats upwards, to surface on the placid loch, as the pale, dawn light reluctantly surrenders to a late-spring day. Watercolour washes in orange and pink give way to wispy-wool clouds gambolling over fresh pastures of azure; reflections mimic their frolicking on clear, blue waters.

There is no breath of wind to cause offence or stir the scene. All is silent.

Any other day, the heart-beat lapping of wavelets against such clinker hull as this would lull a fisher back to early morning slumber, waiting for line to tighten and tiny bell to ring the catch; but, today, goat-frayed mooring-line trailing, the boat drifts aimless on the current, towards glacier-hewn granite shore.

Dipper momentarily rests on gunwale, head bobbing, before once again taking to air, returning to its frantic purpose, hunting amongst ice-cold streams.

In hypnotic, somnolent rhythm, prow tenderly breaks the shimmering surface, before keel scrapes coarse, golden sand, gliding to a halt in shallows, beneath vaulted ceiling of dark green Trossachs forest. Forever in shadow, barren of sunlight, water a deeper green-blue.

In leaf-sieved, piebald light, there's no catch to carry off— nothing reeled into the boat with, or without, struggle; no monster-fish met its end, no tall-tale spun.

Soon, cars will speed along the fresh, black tarmac of the A82, circumnavigating prehistoric waters. Holidaymakers joyfully play at spotting Nessie in the morning light. Locals go about their private business ignorant of drifting vessels, intent on their own frantic purpose, heads bobbing, seeing all yet missing everything for want of a moment's tranquillity; until tomorrow's dawn, when this nexus of stone, water and air will, once more, be silent and alone, washed in watercolours.

# Dance Lesson

## By Karen Ince

"DAMN you to hell!" I scrunched the gorgeous satin skirt into a ball and hurled it in frustration at the door. As it flew, it unfolded and spread like shimmering wings, landing gracefully on the polished floor, mocking me with its sheer unwillingness to satisfy my angry outburst. It lay there, discarded—like my plan for my star pupil. If she turned up for her Thursday class, I'd try again to persuade her.

Mary appeared in the doorway and glanced at the skirt. "I take it that didn't go as planned."

"Understatement." I walked over and picked it up, smoothing the folds of the sumptuous fabric.

"She didn't like it?"

"She loved the skirt. It was the rest of the plan she wasn't so happy about!"

"Then, what …?"

"Apparently I know nothing about my little protégé. I can't believe I've been so stupid! What a way to start the week!"

\* \* \* \* \*

I loved the energy and enthusiasm of the Thursday evening street-dance class. It brought out the best in young teens, especially boys who would often give up on other styles. When I first placed Carrie-Ann in with them, they'd been wary of the age difference, but once they saw her talent, they got over it, and missed her whenever she didn't show up.

If she missed a class, or even a week of classes, she'd always reappear the next week, sporting some kind of injury. Once she arrived with her arm in a cast and an unconvincing story about a car-crash; another time her ankle was swathed in bandages. She'd sat through class, intently memorising a new routine that she performed flawlessly as soon as she could use her leg. She'd justified my belief in her, my investment in her.

I'd taken a risk, entering Carrie-Ann and Danny in such a prestigious competition. But then, it had been a risk when I first partnered them, and that had paid off.

As I put the class through their latest routine, my mind was elsewhere. I could cancel the competition entry. I'd lose the fee, but better that than losing face. I could choose a new partner for Danny. Or a different pair. None of the others were even close to those two. My golden couple. I pictured Danny and Carrie-Ann, dancing together in the sunshine yellow and midnight blue outfits I'd designed, then up on the podium, holding the trophy high. But Carrie-Ann had refused to compete and was now absent from the class.

The lesson came to its noisy, joyful end, and as the pupils were making their way to the changing rooms, I waylaid Danny. "Danny, can I have a word?" He looked at me with the habitual expression of someone who barely tolerates adult intrusion into his important teenage life. "Has your mother spoken to you about the festival?"

He shrugged and nodded. "She said something, yeah."

"What did she tell you?"

"Not much."

"Did she tell you that I've put your name down?"

Danny brightened a bit. "Really? What for?"

"Juvenile couples jive."

Joy swept across his face, like the sun appearing suddenly between clouds, then wariness shadowed it.

"Does she know?"

"I told her after class on Monday."

"Oh." He looked at the floor, watched his right foot tracing a pattern. "What did she say?" he mumbled.

"I wanted to tell you together," I said. "But I thought your mum had already…"

Danny looked me straight in the eye for once. "What did she say?" he persisted.

"Umm, she was… surprised."

"She's not doing it, is she?"

"We-e-ell…"

"That's why she isn't here today!" His words were an arrow, fired at me in anger.

I wasn't about to take the blame for her absence. "It's not the first time…"

"It's the first time she hasn't told *me*!"

57

"What?"

"She always texts me if she's not going to be here. I haven't heard from her all week!"

"It would help if she told me," I snapped. Danny's jaw clenched. "If Carrie-Ann doesn't show up on Monday, you'll have to dance with a new partner."

"No way. I'm not dancing with anyone else." He scowled. "That's not how it works."

"Well, then, maybe you should text her, and tell her she needs to be here on Monday."

"I'm not *telling* her anything. It's not my job."

"Look, Danny, do you want to take part in the competition or not?"

He stared at me, as if I was an alien life-form and he was trying to work out how much of a threat I posed. "Of course, I *want* to," he said, "but I'm not dancing with anyone else. If she's not doing it, I'm not doing it."

"But I've put your names down."

"Well, maybe you should have asked before you did that."

I took a deep breath, keeping my voice calm. "Well, I didn't. I thought you'd both be delighted. It's a great opportunity for you."

"I've gotta go." Danny turned to leave.

"Your mother was pleased."

"I'm sure she was."

"She'll be disappointed if you don't take part."

"She'll get over it. She always does."

"Danny, please. Just think about it, okay?"

He turned back and glared at me. "Think about what? Competing with a new partner? Someone I'm not used to, who doesn't know the routine? Or doing your dirty work for you? Putting pressure on... well, that won't work. If she said no, it's because she can't do it."

"What do you know?"

"Well, I know her name's not Carrie-Ann, for a start off."

"So I discovered on Monday," I said. "What else?"

"She has a pretty tough life, you know. Sometimes she just needs to... y'know... talk about stuff. She messages me." He shrugged and looked at his feet again, as if ashamed of being a good friend.

"What do you know about her home life?" My long-held suspicions surfaced, and my breath caught in my throat.

"I know what she chooses to tell me. If she'd wanted you to know, she'd have told you."

"Do you know where she lives?"

"Why do you want to know?" He was still challenging me. "You never cared before. Now, you want to go and visit her, just to change her mind. You might give her free lessons and stuff, but you don't own her!"

"I want to apologise. I should have thought about her, not just my own ambition for her." Danny stared into my eyes, into my soul. "She's just so damned talented," I blurted, "she deserves a chance to show that off!" I breathed out slowly, recovering my poise. "It has to be her choice. I'm not going to force the issue."

Later, alone in the studio, I could feel the pull of that marvellous skirt, tucked out of sight among voluminous folds of tissue in its box. Packed away, as it would have been for transport to the Festival venue. I lifted it out, shaking out the folds, caressing the bright yellow fabric with my fingertips, admiring the shimmer in the light from the long studio windows, enjoying the dramatic contrast with the deep blue, almost black, top and headpiece.

"Rachel?" Mary's voice broke into my musing. "Thought you might need a cuppa." She was carrying two steaming mugs.

I forced a smile. "Thanks. Although something stronger wouldn't go amiss right now."

"What are you going to do?"

"I still don't know. I've spoken to Danny."

"And ...?"

"He knows more than he's telling. It seems he's always known her real name. He knows she doesn't pay for her lessons. He won't tell me where she lives. He won't put any pressure on her to compete—or even to turn up to class next week."

Mary placed her hand on mine, stopping me from pleating the fine fabric in my agitation. "You're going to have to make a decision soon. You're running out of time to change the names of the competitors." She gently pulled the skirt from me. "I'll just put this away," she commented, folding it efficiently and placing it back among the layers of tissue.

"I know. But I can't imagine anyone else doing as well as those two. When they dance together it's like…"

"Like bread and butter. Made for each other." Mary was always more prosaic than me.

"How can I talk to her when she doesn't come to class, and lied about her address?"

"Stalk her at school? Post her photo on Facebook with a caption saying; 'Has anyone seen this girl?' Walk the streets in the hope that you'll bump into her? I don't know."

"School might be an idea," I said. "But—maybe she lied about that too."

"Then ask her friends. Who does she mix with?"

"That's a… Oh!"

"What?"

"I never thought—she doesn't really. Maybe because she's in a group with older girls. But…"

"Or maybe she goes to a different school? That would make sense, because otherwise, how could she get away with the name thing?" Mary was being practical as always.

"That must be it. But where?"

"Which schools don't we have any other…?"

"Wetherby?"

\* \* \* \* \*

Streams of pupils were coming through the gates. Large groups laughing and joking, jostling each other, letting off the energy that had been penned up in classrooms all afternoon. Twos and threes, not quite so lively but still clearly glad to be out of the confines of lessons. A few solitary figures, mingling among the groups, but obviously alone.

I gripped the ignition key. I could drive away and pretend that I'd never been there. Then I spotted Hollie walking towards the exit with a couple of other girls. The street was thronged with flocks of children and herds of parental vehicles. I wasn't going anywhere in a hurry. When the trio reached the school gates, they put down their bags, and stood chatting. Then Hollie shouldered her backpack, wriggling to adjust the weight on her shoulders. The other two picked up their own bags and set off together, away from school, away from where I sat in my car spying on them. Hollie turned in my direction.

"Hollie?" I called as I got out of the car.

Hollie was startled; for a moment she stood, statue-still, frowning at me.

"Wh…what are you doing here, Miss?"

"I was looking for you, Hollie. You missed your class yesterday. I was worried."

"I'm okay." Hollie shrugged her backpack and stood up tall, as if trying to show me how okay she was.

"Good." I nodded, stuck for anything more eloquent to say. "I can see."

"I need to…" Hollie pointed up the road.

"Yes. Of course."

Neither of us moved. "I could, umm, give you a lift? If you want. That backpack looks…"

Hollie shifted the weight of the pack again. "No. It's fine. I can manage it." Still she didn't move. "Thanks, though. For the offer."

"Hollie, I—"

"I need to go. Mum will be waiting."

"I want to apologise."

"What for? Miss, you've been brilliant. I mean… you know, the classes. Everything. I'm just—" Hollie bit her lip and looked at her feet.

"I shouldn't have pushed you. I should have asked if you wanted to compete."

Tears flickered at the edge of Hollie's eyes as she looked at me. "I do want to," she whispered, swallowing hard. "I can't."

"But you can. You were born to dance. This is a chance to dance in a bigger space, in front of a bigger audience."

"I'm sorry. I know I owe you a lot, and I may never have the money to pay you, but I can't do this."

"It's not about the money." My voice came out harsher than I'd intended. I could feel the tension in my face, in my balled hands.

Hollie cowered away, and I read into that small movement a reflection of a violent home. "I told you already. I can't do the competition. Saturday is housework day. I can't just go missing."

Normally she jumped at every possible opportunity to dance, as if movement and music were the fabric of her very soul. I made a deliberate effort to speak gently. "Can't you just tell your parents you're..." I stopped. "Do your parents know you come to my school?"

Hollie shook her head. "Why haven't you told them?" Hollie shrugged, which I took to mean 'explanations are too complicated'. "Where do they think you are after school on Mondays and Thursdays?" She shrugged again, presumably because she didn't think her parents cared, or maybe even noticed. Teenage sign language seemed to be predominantly different flavours of shrugs.

I wasn't about to give up on her though. Since the day I'd spotted her, outside the windows of the dance studio, mirroring the moves of the class, there'd been something about her that had me hooked. She was one of those rare precious gems among the semi-precious stones which kept me from handing over completely to a younger teacher. This shy, serious young girl had a unique quality, something more than her natural affinity with music, rhythm and movement. It was that quality that had prompted me to offer her free classes. When I saw how she responded, I knew I needed her in my school. Whatever it took.

"What if I spoke to them? Asked their permission for you to dance in the competition?"

"No!" Hollie shouted, unusual behaviour for someone normally so quiet. I realised we were attracting attention.

"Why don't I give you a lift home," I suggested. "I promise I won't come in unless you invite me. We can finish this conversation on the way." I thought she was going to refuse. "I've already made you late. At least let me take you partway."

Hollie nodded, shrugged off her backpack, and we got into the car. "You can give me your address, or the name of a street on the way. But right now, I don't even know which direction to go in."

Hollie silently pointed straight ahead. The street had become a lot emptier while we'd talked, but I still needed to pay attention. "Why don't you want your parents to know about your dancing?"

Hollie stared ahead through the windscreen, not turning to look at me. "There's only my mum." Her voice was toneless.

"And...?"

"And what? That's it. There's just her and me."

"And why don't you want her to know about your dancing?"

Unexpectedly, Hollie started sobbing. "I do want her to know. I want to tell her, but I can't. It would be..."

"What? What would it be?" My lurid imagination went into overdrive; locked rooms, beatings, starvation as punishment for Hollie daring to enjoy herself, for having talent that a mentally disturbed parent could never appreciate.

Hollie's words squeezed through gaps between sobs. "It wouldn't be fair. She was a dancer herself. Before she had me. Before the..."

"What happened?"

"Mum and Dad were out for the evening. They'd left me at Gran's. They had an accident..."

Hollie's words poured into the space, filling the car, spiralling into my ears and my brain. Memories of her father confined to faded photos and grainy video clips. Her mother permanently disabled. The grandmother, who'd done so much for them, suffering with Alzheimer's and in a home. Hollie, balancing school with caring for her mother, with visiting her grandmother who no longer recognised her. Injuries from her mother's wheelchair, or from attempting chores she was too small and inexperienced for.

I blinked and swallowed, gripping the steering wheel, focusing rigidly on the road. I wanted to stop the car, wanted to reach out and hug this brave, beautiful girl, but it seemed that the impersonal space provided by my attention being elsewhere had been the catalyst for Hollie to open up.

"Where does your mum think you go after school?"

"Young carers club."

I stopped at a red light and risked a sideways glance. She was holding herself taut, fighting the raw emotions. I looked ahead again, not wanting to be caught looking.

"But you'd rather dance?"

"Carers club is boring. They teach us to cook, but Gran already did that. They talk about feelings."

"Don't you find that helpful?"

"I have dance."

I knew that feeling. "Do you really think your mum would mind you dancing?"

"It's not fair. I've seen photos. She was so beautiful. She had trophies and everything. She threw them out after... after the accident. When they told her she'd never walk again. But Gran kept some. She gave them to me. They're hidden in my wardrobe."

"Wouldn't she be proud to know you've inherited her talent?"

"It seems like it would be cruel."

"Maybe it would be good for her. To know that her talent lives on in you."

Hollie stared out of the window and sniffled. I drove on, not knowing what I could say. "Next turning on the left," she said.

We turned into a pretty tree-lined street of modern townhouses with wide pavements and flower beds. "Is it much further?"

"Not far now. Go to the end and take the left-hand turn."

I looked around as I drove, contrasting my surroundings to the run-down council estate I'd imagined. I turned left as directed. "Where now?"

"You can stop anywhere here."

I pulled over. "Thanks for the lift," she said, getting out. "And I am sorry about the competition."

"Me too." I tried to smile. "But if you really can't do it, I suppose I'll find another couple."

Hollie gasped. "But you'll still let Danny dance, right?"

I shook my head. "He won't do it without you."

"But that's not fair! He shouldn't miss out because of me."

"I gave him the chance, but he's determined. He'll dance with you, or he won't dance."

"That's not right. You have to make him do it!"

"I wish I could. I wish I could make both of you do it."

There were tears on Hollie's cheeks again. I couldn't ignore her distress any longer. I got out, and gathered her in my arms, stroking her hair. "Shh," I whispered, "he understands. He understood better than me. There'll be other opportunities in the future."

"Not if he's my partner," Hollie sobbed. "But if I stop coming to class, then he'll have to find someone else, won't he?"

"You can't do that! You mustn't."

"I can't deal with making Danny miss out. He's... he's a mate."

"I know. But it's his choice. And to be honest, I'm not sure how well he'd dance with someone else."

"What? He's a great dancer."

"He is. He has a lot of talent, but he never wanted to learn anything until he started dancing with you. You've been good for him."

Hollie looked up at me, her eyes wide. "No! It's him's been good for me. He's helped me to not worry so much about... well, people. What they think about me. What they say about me."

Evidently, I'd never told her before how impressed I was with her effect on our wayward boy. She'd tamed him without trying. "Yes. Not short on self-confidence our Danny, is he? You've been good for each other." I let her go. "You need to get home. Promise me you'll come to class on Monday. I won't change the names for the competition until then, but if you still say no, I'll accept it."

Hollie wiped her face with the back of her hand. "Thanks again for everything, Miss."

"Promise you'll be there on Monday?"

"I promise," she said, with a shaky smile.

As Hollie walked away, I wondered whether she would keep her promise. She disappeared between two houses, and I realised she'd taken an alleyway to another street. I thought about following her and finding out exactly where she did live.

As I drove home I could hear my phone buzzing in my bag on the back seat. When I checked the call log later, I had three missed calls from Danny's mother. I felt the need for a strong cup of tea before calling her back. Mrs Fleming was a force of nature; given her delight at the progress her son had been making since he paired up with Hollie, and her excitement at the news that they would be taking part in a high-profile contest, I dreaded the fallout from the change of plan.

My phone buzzed again. I stifled a sigh as I answered it. "Mrs Fleming. How nice to —" I got no further—she was already in full flow. By the time I'd placated her as best as I could the kettle had boiled and gone cold again. Feeling drained, I decided to treat myself to a takeaway, and a stiff drink while I waited for it. Before

I could act on either intention, my phone rang again. An unrecognised number. It's hard to ignore a call when you run a business, so I pressed the green button.

"Miss?" The word came on a gasp.

"Hollie? Is that you?" There was the sound of ragged breathing, a sniff. "What's the matter?"

"It's my mum."

"What's happened?"

There were a couple of short, sharp intakes of breath, then "She wants to speak to you. I'm passing the phone over."

A new voice, low and a bit croaky, "Miss Simmonds?"

"Yes."

"This is Mrs Weekes. Hollie's mum."

"Hello. It's good to speak to you."

"Hollie was late in from school this afternoon. I was worried about her."

"Yes, I'm sorry—"

"And she looked as though she'd been crying."

"Yes, she—"

"So, I wasn't about to let that pass. Anyway, she's told me."

"Good." I wondered what she'd said.

"I have to apologise for her."

"Apologise? Wh—?"

"Apparently, she's been lying to you. I thought I'd taught her better than that."

"Well, yes, but —"

"I've told her, there's no excuse for lying. And she's been lying to me too. Young carers club, she told me. And all this time she's been… Well. She's got to learn right from wrong. So, I've told her. No more dance classes this term. And no more freebies. We don't need handouts. If you'll send me a bill for the classes she's had, I'll see you get the money."

"No, Mrs Weekes. It's not necessary. It was a pleasure to—"

"Yes. It is necessary. Hollie's told me what you've done for her. And I want you to know how much I appreciate it. And if you're prepared to have her back next term, I'd like to enrol her properly. If that's okay with you. More than she deserves, mind."

"I'd be delighted. Any time. She's... Mrs Weekes, you have to know that—"

"That you wouldn't have gone behind my back if you'd known? I hope not!"

"Oh, well, of course, I wouldn't, but what I wanted to—"

"I'd better give you my real address, then. So you can send me the bill. Got a pen?"

I made a note of the address, wondering if I'd ever get a chance to tell her just how extraordinary her daughter was.

Saturday morning dawned bright and clear, but I really didn't want to get up and face it. At least I didn't have to teach. I'd delegated Saturday morning classes a long time before. The dance school would be thronged with parents, all wanting 'just a quick word'. Children of all ages would be in and out of the changing rooms, the studios, getting in each others' way, shouting and laughing and jostling for attention. Normally I loved it. Today, I would happily give it a miss, but I desperately needed to talk to Mary.

"That's some story," Mary said, blowing out her cheeks in astonishment. "You could make a film out of it."

"I know. But in a film, the insanely attractive, charming and clever dance teacher would come up with a way to persuade the mother to let her daughter enter the competition."

"So, what are you going to do?"

"No idea. I mean, I know I should respect her wishes, but on the other hand, Hollie deserves a shot at the title. Especially now that all the pretence is out of the way."

"You can't interfere, Rachel. And anyway, I thought you'd approve." Mary looked at me with that raised eyebrow she does so well.

"What?"

"How many times have we sat here, and said about kids not having enough discipline these days?"

"Well, yes, I know. But, I mean... Hollie already has it tough. Does she really need to lose out on the one thing that—?"

"What would you do if you discovered that your daughter had been lying—extensively and consistently—to you and other people? Had created a double life for herself?"

"That's not…" I didn't want to admit defeat, but Mary had sound common sense on her side.

"Seriously. Come on. What would you do?"

"I don't know. I'd be horrified. Mortified that she'd done that to someone. I'd be furious."

"Exactly. So however difficult this is for you, you have to allow Mrs Weekes to deal with it."

I tried desperately to come up with a suggestion, or at the very least a justification for trying. "Maybe I'll go and see her next week, during the day so that Hollie's at school. I'll tell her how brilliant Hollie is, I'll persuade her to—"

"Stop! You can't do that!"

"I owe it to Hollie. And Danny. I have to at least try."

"No! You can't come between a parent and child. You have to accept Mrs Weekes' decision on this. At least she's letting Hollie come here properly next term. She could have banned her completely. She could be asking how you let a girl register with a false name and address!"

We sipped our tea. She was right—as usual. "I thought I'd learnt something. But actually, I still just want everyone to dance to my tune."

Mary put her hand on my shoulder. "You're a determined woman who's built a successful school from nothing and wants only the best for her pupils."

"I'm a selfish old bat, who's used to getting her own way."

Mary smiled at that, and then spoke gently. "Why don't you hand deliver that invoice to Hollie's mum, while Hollie's at school. And let her know that you support her decision. If you want Hollie back here next term, you need to build bridges."

I tried to give in gracefully. I'm not sure how well the graceful bit worked. "You're right, of course. Now I need to decide what to do about that competition. And Danny. Who's he going to dance with for the rest of the term?"

"Oh, yes. Danny. He'll no doubt have his own ideas."

"And he won't make it easy for me!"

# Dark Blue

## By Anne Sikora Lord

"Spare a few coppers, mate?"

Focused on my day ahead, I had not noticed the figure hunched under an ageing grey blanket, sitting in a shop doorway next to the bank on Main Street. Beside him was a sad-looking skinny mutt. Curled up close to the already donated offerings of a Saturday morning, canine eyes looking up at me, pleading.

Shocked, aghast, I knew the voice—how could I not? Older now, gravelly, with the liquid, hacking cough of a smoker. I froze, teetering, hovering between pretending not to hear and just running.

The voice took me back to a day when my life really had stood still. The full horror of a child gone missing. A four-year-old, too young to defend herself, or even understand the situation.

I was on duty when the panicked call came through, Beth, our childminder, in tears.

"We were watching kiddies tv... no one noticed her creep downstairs," she gasped. "I thought she was in her bedroom... I'm so sorry..."

"Listen," I butted in. "Calm down Beth, it'll be okay."

She went quiet.

"Have you searched the house properly? You know how she likes to hide."

"Yes, yes. And the garden." She sniffed back tears and drew in a deep breath.

"How long has she been gone, Beth?"

"I don't know, I can't be sure—hours maybe. Oh God... I'm sorry..."

My heart lurched, my pulse quickened, but I managed to get my brain in gear. Crisis mode. "You need to ring the nick straight away. They'll want descriptions, times, locations. It will set procedures in motion... are you listening to me, Beth?"

She started to cry again. I was having a hard time myself, trying to hold it together. My brain hammered, stomach churning, vision blurring, as adrenaline coursed through my blood. But, trying to stop my voice from cracking, I shouted into the mobile— "Just do it, Beth. NOW!"

I cut the line and switched to the radio. Gus Brown, my patrol sergeant, heard my call sign, and probably caught the panic in my voice. Having rapidly given him the basic details, he then went quiet for what seemed an age. I could hear muted voices in the background. *Hurry, please,* I repeated in my head, *my beautiful daughter is missing!*

"Yup, Beth's on the line," he confirmed, "Don't worry—we've got this. We'll keep you updated once we've let HQ know. Best get home."

I ignored the last bit. Against all advice I took part in the search—I would dare them to stop me. Despite what you see on television regarding missing people, a vulnerable child, a confused pensioner, or a person who is a danger to themselves or others, necessitates immediate action. I knew how vital it was to find her soon, each minute of the 'golden hour' which passed reduced the chance of a good outcome.

Everyone available was out looking, including CID, the dog unit, those of my fellow officers about to go off duty.

I thought about her sweet little face, bouncing blonde curls, the daisy-print blue dress she had chosen herself on a day out shopping—the flowers her namesake.

Thrilled with her purchase she had skipped down the road, insisting she wore it that same day, to go with her older brother and sister and get sweets at the village shop. It was so unlike her to wander off.

*Daisy! Daisy Daisy! Where are you?*

There was no need for photos, she was known to everyone, police and villagers alike, but after no immediate luck at finding her, they were distributed anyway.

It seemed the whole of our neighbourhood had turned out to help with the search. That's what it was like back then, a real community. Fear ran through everyone—it wasn't the first time a child had gone missing. Gardens were searched, shed contents turned over, garages checked. The local recreation ground, the coppice, the banks of the canal. Divers would be on their way, I thought. I didn't envy their job of searching the cold depths of the canal, and a short while later, was filled with gratitude when I watched them submerge themselves time and again, but silently prayed—*please don't find her*. I couldn't bear the thought of seeing them retrieving her limp little body. I walked back to my vehicle and made my way home, needing to check how the rest of the family were coping.

As I got out of the patrol car, Mr Edwards, our elderly neighbour, shuffled down his path. He stood rubbing his ailing back, watching me as I approached.

"I've gone through my gardens, front and back," he called, offering some reassurance that he was doing his bit, "looking under the bushes and hedges. You know what children are like." Gently patting his arthritic hand that was resting on his gate, I thanked him.

"You're a good man, Bill," I said, giving him a thumbs up as I walked away towards my own driveway.

Even Betty Graham, who had an ingrained dislike of the police, on account of both her sons being inside for their sins, came out of her house carrying a tray of steaming mugs.

"Come on each of youse… get yersels a cuppa," she ordered. "It's allus bloody parky this time a day," she continued, stating the obvious.

I turned down the offered mug of tea, but thanked Betty for her kindness and made my way to my own front door. Slipping my key into the lock, and shouldering the sticking front door open, I found two forlorn faces staring back at me, craning to see if Daisy was behind me. Jack and Ella, their disappointment obvious, fired questions at me.

"You will find her, won't you?" demanded Jack.

"I'm not going to bed… ever… until she's home," stated Ella.

I didn't know what to say. I couldn't lie. I wanted to say, 'Of course I will…'; 'I won't stop until I have found her…'; 'I will bring your precious sister home!'

Instead, I held them close, hugging them, planting a kiss on each of their heads. I whispered how much I loved them into their shampoo-scented hair. My heart lurched—*What if she never comes home? What will I say then?* I reluctantly released them.

"Go and get into your pyjamas. I'm going straight back out there once I've picked up a sandwich, and be good for Beth, won't you?" They nodded simultaneously and ran upstairs to get ready for bed.

I got back into my car to continue my search, intending to explore further afield.

As hours went by, day became night and flashes of torchlight continued to rake across fields, trees. Beams strafed the surface of oily, grim water. My despair deepened as I lurched from pessimism to hope, and back again.

*We're not going to find her. We must find her!*

The task seemed immense. She could be anywhere. Just before midnight my mobile rang. It was Gus. My finger trembled as I aimed at the green icon. My radio crackled in the background, I turned down the volume to focus on Gus.

"Sarge? What's happening? Has she been found?" I gasped, firing questions, desperate for good news.

"Take a breath," he ordered. "We've got her."

"Thank God." My shoulders dropped with relief. "Is she okay?"

"I've only bare details at the moment, but we're standing everyone down." I choked back tears as muscle tension began to subside.

Gus continued, "An officer on door-to-door enquiries heard a child whimpering in the background when questioning a neighbour. It appears that Daisy was with a man who said he found her wandering in the street and had taken her in."

"But she's been gone hours, Gus," I interrupted. "When did he find her? Why didn't he report it?"

"Exactly. This is why the officer thought the circumstances suspicious and called it in straight away for a further look. The search and forensics teams are being ordered to close in on the property as we speak."

I raced home to find a sobbing Daisy, shoulders heaving, face red and eyes puffy. Tears had tracked dirt trails down her cheeks, snot bubbling from her nose. My heart clenched as she ran from Beth's arms to mine. I held her close for a long, long time.

Despite examination, followed by sensitive interviewing by the best special investigations officers, we never knew the extent of what he had done to her, unable to be sure. She was so young, too

72

innocent to understand. But, we all knew this was not an isolated incident. There had been others. He had previous, a man with a record.

Initial relief at finding her had quickly been replaced by so many emotions; disbelief, guilt at not being there for her, grief, and finally anger, a raging hatred of those who preyed on children. No one would touch my little girl and get away with it but get away with it he did. A technicality at court.

As I sat straining my ears, listening to the lawyers and judge, their heads together discussing 'Points of law...'; 'Flimsy evidence...'; 'Circumstantial at the most...'; 'An unsafe verdict...' my fists clenched and unclenched. A sense of foreboding crept over me. I could see the way this was going. Dull embers of anger began to glow hot in my veins, fury driving me upwards, thrusting me forward out of my seat.

"You've got to be kidding me," I heard a strange version of my own voice, "No, no, NO!"

Tight grips on both arms prevented me from launching myself as I was propelled out of the courtroom without as much as a nod to the judge's affronted expression.

In the fresh air, Gus and a security guy stood either side of me. Weighty hands on my shoulders, pushing me down, my backside thudding on the unforgiving marble bench. I slumped, head held in my hands, wretched. I was spent. The anguish, frustration, and torment that had built up during the months prior to the court case had taken its toll. My fists balled; my knuckles, not just white, but numb. A madness burned in my belly like a wildfire, uncontrolled. When he appeared, bounding down the steps with his lawyer, evading reporters and leaping into a waiting taxi, I wanted to smash his smug face in. In those few anger fuelled moments I decided—he was not going to escape punishment. I wanted revenge.

I planned. I followed. I watched. Logging his patterns of behaviour; who he mixed with, where he went, where he bought his booze and fags. I became obsessed. No matter how hard I tried, I knew I couldn't let it go, determined not to allow it to happen again to someone else's child. In my head lived a malevolent phantom, invading my thoughts with stealth. I was no longer me!

It was easy in a police car on patrol. He knew he would be watched, but mostly I shadowed him off duty. The only guaranteed regular thing he did was visit his local every Friday night. I followed him for several weeks, timed him, tracked his route back home. Most of his swaying, drunken journey at the end of the evening was well lit, too many people around, but eventually a plan began to take shape.

Halfway home he would cut through a deserted building site. The developers had gone bust, new builds abandoned, a ghost town remote enough to do what I had to do without being seen.

Autumn into winter, the clocks had just gone back. It had been tipping down, claggy mud made the site slippery. Eerie windowless buildings, and half constructed walls gave an appearance of empty eyes and gaping teeth. Tarpaulin flapping in the breeze, whipping and cracking like yacht sails. Clothes dark, gloves on. Baseball cap pulled low, hoodie pulled up. I located the green and slimy spade, long-discarded by the construction workers, a tool I had previously secreted away amongst rubble.

Waiting in the darkness at a corner where I knew he would pass, my heart quickened. I smelt the cigarette smoke first, the scent carried in drifts on the wind. I could hear him coming closer, whistling, unsteady footfall. Something in me stirred—the adrenaline took over. My vision blurred. I began to sweat. Without realising it I had raised the spade. This was not me! The gentle local bobby, turned into a vengeful monster. The demons in my head soared, took over and timed it just right. The spade swung back in an arc, adjusting height, flying forward. It hit its target perfectly— the crunch of flesh and bone unmistakable.

Not even a grunt. He went down like a slaughtered pig, hitting the concrete pilings with a resounding clump. There wouldn't have been time for a shocked look, a moment of confusion. Pity that, the beast in my head thought, as I rained down further blows with the spade until he screamed. I kicked, imagining his kidneys bleeding. I stamped, and stamped again, as he writhed like a dying cockroach. I dealt a couple more blows for good measure until he stopped moving. Dead still, a whimper escaped. Attempting to move, he cried out like a child. *Now you know what pain feels like! A different kind to the one you caused, but pain all the same.*

74

I didn't even take a closer look to see the damage. I knew his face would be pulp. I just ran and kept on running, throwing the spade into the depths of the close by canal, before heading for home.

Fear gripped me for several weeks, the dread of being discovered.

There was a perfunctory investigation, but detectives were overrun with cases, short-staffed. No one could be bothered to prioritise the apparent mugging gone wrong, especially of an alleged sex offender. 'Had it coming to him...'; 'Karma if you ask me...'; and 'Scum of the earth' were the most frequent snippets I heard as I monitored their progress.

Each day I would sigh with relief as the paperwork became buried deeper. If anyone found the spade, any DNA or other evidence would likely be long gone. Eventually the file was consigned to the bottom of a green metal filing cabinet with the rest of the cold cases on division.

Gradually, the tension in my shoulders began to subside. I no longer twisted and wrung my hands, or looked over my shoulder waiting to be apprehended by my governor. The balled fists slowly uncurled as the anger seeped away, and my demeanour returned to somewhere near the calmness prior to Daisy's abduction. But anger and fear had been replaced by another emotion that gnawed away at night—guilt! I never told anyone. I just tucked it away in the recesses of my mind, along with the demons that had taken over that night. I went back to patrolling the streets and keeping the peace and never saw that monster again.

Until today!

"Spare a few coppers, mate?" he repeated to my immovable feet, not even bothering to raise his head.

"S-s-sorry..." I stuttered. "I haven't any change." I never knew what to say to down-and-outs other than "Move along there." I tried to gather myself, get it together, shift, but remained in stasis, captured in the moment. He looked up, sensing my hesitation. Bile rose in my throat. Jesus, had I done that much damage? One crooked eye, limpid in its socket, struggling to focus. The other, just an empty orbit, sunken skin, hollow. A boxer's nose, flattened above twisted lips and a sideways jaw.

"Don't worry, love. Next time, maybe?" He attempted a smile, pulling the scar-stretched skin into more of a grimace. He clearly hadn't recognised me. He would have seen me in court, on the steps outside. Maybe even on the building site?

I nodded, thrust my shaking hands into my pockets and moved on. It was true, I didn't have any loose change to give him, but the guilt had returned. Great swathes of shame smothered me. What had I done? Acting as judge and jury, instead of abiding by my oath, to serve and protect? I pulled out a twenty-pound note at the nearest 24/7 and purchased several cans of dog food, making sure they had ring pulls.

I couldn't make things right, nor did I want to, for him at least, but I was sure as hell not going to let a dog suffer. Some would say revenge is sweet, but there are always consequences. Guilt was something I would have to learn to live with for the rest of my life.

Returning, keeping my face hidden, I placed the tins in front of the dog and cast the remaining change into the 'begging bowl'—a soft flat cap.

"God bless you, miss." The shock in his voice at the amount tossed down in front of him was unmistakeable.

God bless me indeed, I thought. If he only knew. I turned and walked away.

# DECONSTRUCTING OLD STUFF

## BY ANNE SIKORA LORD

*(A "FOUND" POEM)*

MUSEUMS are where old stuff goes
Storehouses of artefacts and specimens
More than just buildings
Treasure troves held within.

The fantastic hoards they preserve
Human past, material remains,
Wonder rooms
Cabinets of curiosity,
Physical and metaphysical,
In trust for society
Heritage of humanity and the environment.

Museums are about where we were as people
Where we fit into a larger scheme of things
In terms of past and future
To take away not just information
But something deeply spiritual, emotional;
Hands on, interactive experiences,
That inspire and thrill.

They can make you feel good,
Smarter, inspired, excited.
They can make you feel sad,
Horrified, guilty, ashamed.

Museums are the seat of the muses
And are not always universal,
They may not serve everyone equally.
Not objective truth but histories we choose to display,
Fable agreed upon by the winners of war;
Imperialism, colonialism and other '-isms' dictate
A dark heart within a collection
Enforcing archaic ideas
Or offensive attitudes
A series of stories we create ourselves,
Those we've been telling over the years

Museums must tell it in context
With integrity in our interpretation.
Together with spaces for multiple voices
Not excusing the past but acknowledging impact
Not demonising nor simplifying into good and bad

But collaborating with, not for, communities.
Repatriating artefacts to original nations
Objects and cultures intrinsically linked
Facts can be woven into stories
More exciting and engaging
We've been doing it all our lives.

Museums can translate experiences
Across the blue of space and time.
We can change ourselves by changing the stories we tell
Affecting the fundamental sense of self
Allowing everyone identity
About where we are as people now.
Understanding of the past
Preventing future mistakes
The relevance to present life
Reinterpreted for future generations, this generation
How far we have come, or not!

## DEFLATING WALTER

### BY DON MUNNINGS

THE 'Blue Dolphin' had just moored, and the crew were unloading the catch. Walter swaggered over and watched them through half-closed eyes, his belly casting a shadow over the sparkling water.

"And what have you got for me today, lads?" he boomed.

"Some good stuff today, Mr Harbinger," Bert, the skipper, told him. "Cod, plaice, a few nice dabs, and something for the centre of your display slab." He pointed to a box containing a conger eel, weighing at least thirty pounds, still wriggling, and glaring wickedly at all and sundry.

Walter hid his delight. Such a fish would certainly draw punters to his shop window. He could picture it surrounded by mackerel, bass and other smaller fish. With crabs, lobsters and oysters artistically sprinkled amongst them.

A crowd gathered on the quay to watch Walter's legendry haggling skills. Having beaten the fisherman down to a ridiculously low price for the conger, his attention turned to a box of assorted smaller fish. Reaching down he seized a small plaice and held it disdainfully in front of Bert's face. "Call this a plaice, lad?" he said loudly. "I've seen bigger postage stamps."

The plaice, smarting under the insult and taking an instant dislike to Walter, made a last bid for freedom—slipped from his grasp and fell to the ground. Walter tried to grab it, staggered, trod on it, and slipped backside-first into the box containing the conger.

Having suffered many indignities over the last few hours, the conger had been plotting revenge. The appearance of a well-trousered, plump derriere, thrust right into its face, was more than it could have hoped for.

Walter's features ran the gamut of emotions: surprise, indignation, and embarrassment, turning to pain and terror. With a banshee wail he rose from the box like a Saturn V rocket leaving the launching pad, the conger's teeth firmly attached to one buttock. Have you ever seen a dog catch sight of its tail and start chasing it? Then you'll have some idea of the antics Walter performed before a delighted crowd.

The conger, its mission accomplished and starting to feel rather dizzy, released Walter and slid over the edge of the quay. It couldn't wait to seek the company of other fish, to regale them with stories of its derring-do, and the savaging of fat fishmongers.

Walter staggered to the railings and slumped over them, moaning pitifully.

In the confusion there were other casualties: Jock the grocer laughed so much he had a heart attack; a small boy fell into the water; a box of fish was dropped on someone's foot; and two WI ladies running a charity stall peed themselves.

The wailing of ambulance sirens brought dozens of townsfolk rushing to the quay to find scenes of carnage reminiscent of a bomb having been dropped.

Walter remained supported by the railings, gently sobbing, and shaking like a leaf, well aware of the extensive damage to his favourite pair of strides and what lay beneath them. The paramedics, egged on by a knowledgeable crowd of bystanders, laid him face-down on the stretcher and applied surgical dressings. So moved were they by Walter's plight they had tears streaming down their faces and seemed to be shaking with emotion.

It was some weeks before Walter felt fit or confident enough to resume his position behind the display slab. His young assistant had excelled himself in his absence. The display looked superb and customers flocked to the shop… but not, it seemed, to buy fish. They kept giving sidelong glances at Walter and he distinctly heard one of them whisper, "That's him, over there. The one who had his arse bitten by a fish!"

## DOROTHY

### BY NIKI SAKKA

THE clock tower strikes ten a.m. Dorothy is here, again! She is punctual, as always.

A big, heavy, blue, plastic bag is hanging down from her left shoulder. It's tied up with a black belt and it's well secured around her waist. Her clothes are loose on her, and dirty, and her grey hair is tangled.

She looks around. The daily meeting is about to start, for sure. The other members of this mannequin committee are all there, inside the display window. Dorothy looks straight into their eyes. It seems that an interesting, silent conversation has just started. Is it about global warming? Is it about politics? Is it about education changes? Or is it about the latest fashion? That seems most likely, but who knows?

In front of the next-door shops lorries are unloading. On the main road, cars move slowly up the hill and others speed down in the opposite direction. Pigeons and seagulls fly overhead, showing off in their own performance. People are walking up and down the pavements. Others are crossing the road. A few metres away, three people stand, chatting, in the middle of the pavement. Around Dorothy, people are looking through the window at the ladieswear display, while others are coming in and out of the shop. The shop assistants inside are busy helping them. Soft music adds a calming, pleasant feeling in the shop.

Dorothy, with her pale, tired and unsmiling face, is still there. Her thin lips are tight and sunken inside her mouth without the support of her teeth. Her blue eyes stare at the mannequins who are standing just opposite, only a glass window apart. Their conversation carries on. Nothing disturbs it.

The double door of the shop is open. I'm standing beside it observing this fascinating meeting. I have a bit of spare time today, so, I believe it's my chance to get to know more about Dorothy, to get insight into those daily meetings, those endless silent conversations. I'm also curious what is inside her blue bag! Are there keys for a house or car? I don't think so. She looks homeless to me. What about medication? Is she suffering from a chronic illness and needs daily medication? God knows! Perhaps she's got some photographs of family members, or her children. That is, if she even has any family. She definitely has a note pad and pen. Over the years I have seen her using them a number of times. I wonder if she owns anything apart from whatever there is in this bag. Will I ever be able to find out who she really is? Above all, will I ever find out what her real name is?

During a laconic conversation with Dorothy, I had discovered that under the disorderly appearance was a sweet personality and, I believed, a pure soul.

It's a new day. The clock tower strikes ten a.m. Dorothy is here for the daily meeting and the silent conversation with the mannequins. Her clothes are clean and her face lights up with a smile when I wave hello to her. From that day on, after her meeting, if there were no customers inside the shop she would rush in, stand

81

at the back like a frozen statue for a few minutes, and then shoot out again.

One day she leaves a family photograph on the counter in front of me before going out of the shop. It is a picture of a handsome, well-dressed man cuddling a preschool boy and a toddler girl. I turn it over, and discover, neatly written on the back:

*You are my heart, my love,*
*Joy, happiness and fun.*
*You are my wealth, my treasure,*
*And the breeze of a fresh air.*
*You mean everything to me,*
*Believe me!*

*With all my love*
*your dear wife and your dearest mum*
*xxx*

The next morning Dorothy fails to attend her daily meeting. And the day after, and the day after that. Forever...

## FIGURES

### BY CAROL SALTER

FROM my seat in the bow window of the café bar which faced the busy junction, I watched a woman appear, pedalling a silver bicycle like a lunatic. Her behaviour attracted my attention; that and her unusual attire. A blue kerchief, tied at the back of her head, covered her face from the bridge of her nose to below her chin.

My suspicion of her disregard for personal safety was confirmed by the lack of a cycle helmet. She'd opted instead for an Australian bush hat in which her hair was captured. I was surprised by the coat too, a full-length leather duster, the type folk use to conceal shotguns in films. The length of it would have been cumbersome to most whilst cycling, but she didn't display any outward difficulties.

Cutting across the cycle lane at a right angle, she braked hard. Her cavalier movement caused her cycle to slew sideways, spraying gutter gravel high into the air; an action which prompted several disapproving glares from drivers and pedestrians alike. A gap appeared in the traffic. She sailed through, seemingly oblivious to her earlier manoeuvre and uncaring of any harm.

Turning right onto the High Street, she cycled leisurely in my direction. I was captivated. Her head swivelled left and right, her eyes sizing up various hostelries, whilst ignoring the growing number of vehicles tailing at snail's pace behind.

Securing her bike to the railings outside, she sauntered into the café bar like she owned the place. Up close, I guessed she was slightly younger than me, maybe in her mid-twenties, judging by her physique. Two steps inside the building a youth returning from the men's room waylaid her, blocking her progress to the counter. His eyes travelled the length of her form giving her an admiring gaze. Even wearing the coat, which she'd unbuttoned as she entered, her hour-glass shape was obvious.

I didn't hear what she said to the youth, but the look on his face said it all. He slumped down in his chair, crestfallen and glum, eyes to the floor. A swig from his beer didn't seem to help matters. He downed the dregs in his glass, rose and left. *What on Earth did she say to him that made him leave?* Whatever it was had sapped his confidence, that much was clear.

Ignoring his exit, the woman stood just inside the doorway perusing the drinks list painted high on the far wall. I moved from my spot in the window when advised my food was ready at the counter. I preferred to eat at the counter rather than on display to the passing public like some exhibit in a pet shop window.

Finishing her beverage assessment, the woman lifted both hands and removed her hat. A river of sunshine blonde hair escaped, cascading in long wavy tresses which surrounded her in bouncing energy. I wasn't the only man to gape. A few more heads turned her way, the bar being filled predominantly with men this particular lunchtime. It was a bizarre reaction to what was, on the surface, a perfectly ordinary action, but this woman was anything but ordinary.

It was her eyes. Deep, penetrating blue eyes. Eyes that peered into your soul. Eyes which had seen the world and said, 'Is that all you have? I want more.' Eyes that pulled you in and twisted your heart. Hers met mine. She blinked and I had the satisfaction of knowing she tore her gaze away first, in pretence of jamming her hat in her coat pocket. That done, she strode, purposeful and confident, towards the counter.

Taking the empty seat to my left, she ordered tea with milk from the assistant. *English, but something else too,* I surmised, trying to place her accent. In moments, her drink arrived. I realised then a second man, sitting to her left, was as fixated as me on this kerchief-covered female.

I watched his hungry eyes. They followed her slender fingers to her coat pocket to retrieve a drawstring purse. *Is he interested in her money?* Strangely, she smiled; the skin crinkling at the corner of her eyes. I imagined full luscious lips parting and lifting at the edges beneath her curious face covering. The bandana created an aura of mystery which irritated and fascinated me in equal measure. This woman was an enigma and I enjoyed solving puzzles.

The arrival of her tea meant she'd have to remove her kerchief to drink. We both watched spellbound as she set about preparing her tea. She frowned momentarily, staring down at the dry teabag in her cup. *Maybe, she doesn't realise that in this café bar they serve the hot water separately. That means she doesn't come here regularly. Should I help her?* Then her frown cleared, her eyes lit up and she reached for the water pot, lifting the lid to check inside. We were mesmerised by her actions. As she lifted the pot, she paused, her hand in mid-air, giving us each a sideways glance before continuing her simple preparations.

The tea made, we waited expectantly for the unveiling. Moving her hands behind her head, she appeared to tighten the knot holding the kerchief in place, rather than loosen it. *A blatant tease.* I still held my breath like some kid on Christmas morning unwrapping the biggest present.

One hand lifted the cup, the other lifted the material away from her face. She slipped the cup underneath. It was a practice born of experience. She had no intention of removing that kerchief. Every guess I'd made so far about this woman had been wrong. I was disappointed and annoyed with myself for being so engrossed in a total stranger.

Because of my obsession, I'd completely forgotten my own food and drink, both now cooling rapidly. I heard her supping on the tea and imagined perfect full lips sealed along the cup's hard rim. I shook my head in exasperation of my adolescent fantasy. I hadn't had thoughts like this in forever.

She drank her tea whilst I returned to my meal, my appetite lost. The man on her left, took a half-hearted slug of his beer. Careless in his actions from watching her, he slopped it over himself and the counter. I heard him swearing under his breath, as he wiped at his shirt, not noticing the beer dripping over the counter edge and down onto his trousers. I smiled at his ineptitude, his plight making me feel better.

Tea finished, the cup re-appeared and settled on the counter. Next, she swivelled on her stool to face the beer-stained fellow. It took all my resolve not to demand she face me. *How dare she choose him over me!* I seethed inside, my body growing tense.

"You okay?" asked the assistant, misinterpreting my frustrated expression as he continued to dry the perennial glass. "Only, you don't look so…" He searched for the right word, "…well."

"I'm fine," I reassured him. "Something must have gone down the wrong way." I gestured towards my plate. His gaze hardened and a frown appeared. *Shit!* I'd upset him, implying his food was to blame.

"The food is great," I added lamely, sure he could see through my attempt at flattery. I gave him a double thumbs-up to stress my point. A weak smile replaced his frown, and his eyes lost that hard edge from moments ago.

"If you're sure?" he insisted, needing further reassurance. I nodded several times more in quick succession and, satisfied, he moved away to serve someone else.

Common sense returned fleetingly. *What is wrong with me? Am I going mad? Why am I obsessing about this woman? I don't know her. Do I?*

I'd missed the woman swinging around to face me while I spoke to the assistant. From the appraising stare she gave me, I imagined she could tell that I'd lied. She turned back to my opponent without a word. *How dare she judge me?*

"Do you know if any fig trees grow hereabouts?" She asked of my competitor, her voice soft and melodious. *What a bizarre question. Definitely English, threaded with some intangible accent.* Seeing the blank look on his face she began again.

"They're gnarly weaving trees, with leaves shaped like this." Her delicate fingers spread out in a fan-like shape capturing his gaze. Her hands were perfect.

*I know where a fig tree grows locally. Why doesn't she ask me? Why ask that imbecile? He wouldn't know a fig from an oak if the tree fell on him. Ask me. Go on ask me!*

The woman continued to ignore me, apparently preferring this insipid man instead. I was outraged. *Get a hold of yourself Fred. You could get any woman you wanted. You just don't want—anymore.* I was arguing with myself over a woman I didn't even know. It was ludicrous. I was ludicrous, but I couldn't stop. *I know, but I want this one. This one is important.*

The fool stared at her, trapped like a rabbit in the proverbial headlights. He was smitten. An idiotic smile was plastered across his face. Like the earlier fellow, he couldn't give her what she wanted. My heart pounded. My brain screamed. *Tell her. Tell her you know.*

"I know where a fig tree grows," I blurted out, to the back of her head. *Not the greatest chat-up line Fred.* She didn't turn around, as I hoped, and thank me profusely. Her head tilted like a bird listening, causing the luscious curls to bounce to one side. I wanted to touch them, run the smooth locks between my fingers. I drew in a deep breath—bated. She turned deliberately slowly on her stool to face me. I gazed triumphantly over her shoulder at my demoralised foe.

"What would you know about local flora?" Her verbal attack took me off guard. "You don't come from here. You're just passing

86

through, on your way to other lucrative business." *How can she know that?*

"H...h...how can you know that?" I stuttered, the words echoing those in my mind, my confidence taken aback by her animosity.

"Your clothing is more suited to city life, than rural. The meal you've chosen is usual in more northern climes. You like your coffee strong, like the eastern tribes. Your accent, though cosmopolitan through travel," she added, "disguises a western twang." Seeing my face drop, her eyes smiled. "Need I go on?" I shook my head unable to speak in the face of perfection. I could see why the other lad had left. This woman was a Valkyrie. The man opposite sniggered, like a pathetic adolescent. I glared at him, his reaction making me more determined to win this battle.

"Still, if you know where a fig tree grows," she acknowledged. "I shall listen."

I raised my head as the man sloped away, hands in pockets, shoulders slumped in defeat. I grinned like a cat given its freedom to play, wanting to fist-pump the air in triumph.

"The private Wayside Estate in Chistleton," I mumbled. Her eyes, the colour of sapphires, bore into mine as if divining the truth of my words. Nothing. No reaction, no response, no thanks. Then I realised, she was waiting for directions.

"It's a little difficult to find or give directions," I lied. Wayside was easy to find.

"How come you know where it is, if you don't live here?"

I was hypnotised. *When is she going to take that blasted kerchief off?*

Catching my gaze, her eyes crinkled once more and she answered, divining my thoughts again, "I never take this off." Then, realising I wasn't going to speak, she continued, "I have..." She reached for the words, "unusual teeth."

*What the hell does that mean? Buck teeth, missing teeth, brown teeth.* A gamut of dental problems paraded across my mind. She didn't move. *What is she waiting for?* I very nearly exclaimed, "I don't care! Give me those elusive lips." But I didn't. I sat trying hard to marshal my emotions.

"The Wayside Estate?" she prompted.

87

"Yes, it belongs to me," I stumbled over my words. "Well, until I sell it." Her eyes widened. "It's the reason I'm here."

In seconds, her body posture transformed from assertive woman to terrified girl and back again. These micro-emotions flickered through her eyes too, then vanished completely to be replaced by something else, something warrior-like. It was as if she'd met her worst nightmare and decided to fight it head on. She rose from her seat, her posture straightening further. Her shoulders tensing back, thrusting her chest out. She fisted her hands. I thought for a moment that she was going to punch me. I longed to rip off that bloody kerchief and make her mine despite the audience. The savage thought thrilled and frightened me, my heart racing in anticipation.

When I steadied my thoughts, a warrior woman stood facing me, staring down at me as I sat. Standing taller than I remembered, her delicate hands lifted, her fingers rearranging and re-tying her kerchief without removing it. I swear I glimpsed two rows of perfectly pointed teeth. It was an illusion, it had to be, created by my over-worked imagination and brought about by the confrontational situation.

"Thank you for your information, but I cannot use that particular fig tree. Its use has been rescinded."

*What the hell does that even mean?* As I sat trying to understand her statement, the mystery woman paid for her tea and left without a backward glance.

The last I saw of her was as she cycled back across town, her leather coat flying. Something iridescent glimmered within its lining. *What is that?* It's outline resembled a dragonfly's wing. I noted her direction of travel, heading towards Chistleton. *And, if I'm not mistaken, the Wayside Estate.* Despite what she had said to me.

\* \* \* \* \*

I sat in the upstairs window waiting. *She will come, I just need to be patient.* The moment she'd disappeared around the corner, I'd paid my bill, rushed to my car and driven to my grandfather's house, knowing my combustion engine could easily beat her.

I hadn't been in my grandfather's home for a decade. It still smelt of him—old musty books and the stink of cigars long

88

extinguished, dominated the furnishings. I'd been named Alfred after him, but preferred to be called Fred, feeling Alfred sounded like it belonged to an old man.

The house was old long before Alfred inherited it from his own grandfather, also named Alfred. The twisted fig tree, at least as old as the house, leant against the sunlit back wall. When I arrived, I immediately visited the tree and quickly paid my respects, a ridiculous family tradition taught by my grandpa.

*There isn't anything remarkable about the tree. What makes it so interesting?* I stared up at the wayward branches. *She'd said it was 'rescinded.'* I didn't know what that meant. I saw she wanted it though, despite the words that fell from her mouth. There was avarice in her gaze before she left. I knew that feeling of desire, of wanting to possess something. *What does she need it for? It's not in fruit. It's not a rare variety.*

While I waited, I got out my phone. My grandfather had taken great pains to drill the type and variety of tree into my brain as a child. I hadn't a clue why the tree was so important to him. Whenever my parents and I visited, he'd first take us to stand in front of the tree and pay our respects. I'd thought he was a bit looney when I was a child; eccentric, I discovered, was the word my family used. My mother encouraged me to humour him, telling me he'd done the same thing to her ever since the disappearance of her own mother, his wife Lily, when she was a young child.

"Icus Carica Doree, is a variety of fig dating back to the 17th Century," I read out loud from Google. *That could make it as old as the house.* "It produces fruit twice a year, mid-June and mid-September." *It's late April.*

I missed her arrival, my head down, staring at the web browser. I looked up to see her silver bicycle propped against the low front wall. She was nowhere in sight. I'd expected her to ring the doorbell.

A memory surfaced, my mother telling me a few years back, that I'd miss my own funeral. I smiled at the memory seeing her beautiful face once more in my mind. My mother Sophie was gone, my father too and both grandparents. I'd missed every one of their deaths and felt that guilt every day. I hadn't been there for any of them. Each had already been laid to rest before my flights arrived back in England. Now I was alone, no siblings, my partner gone too. Nothing, except my work at the publishing company. It was a lonely bleak existence.

*I should have known she wouldn't do anything like a normal person.* It galvanised me into action. *Where is she?* I clambered like a hippo down the stairs, stiff from sitting in one position so long, heading towards the garden via the back of the house.

She stood there, in front of the fig—my fig. Arms wide, just like my grandfather had made me do countless times. *How can she know that? Nobody knows that ritual except us. It's our secret family tradition.* Yet here she was, paying her respects to our tree. And the tree appeared to be listening. Its lower branches drooped, touching her shoulders in a light caress.

Stealing down the back steps, I crossed the lawn, my bottom jaw dropping. In front of her the tree seemed to shimmer, its outline blurring. I rubbed my eyes in disbelief.

"This isn't happening." She either didn't hear me or ignored me. Thinking on our earlier interaction, probably the latter. "It's alive?"

"Yes, of course it is," she replied. "And it misses you," she added, turning to face me. "When did you last pay your respects, apart from today?"

I ignored the accusation in her tone, distracted by the sight of her kerchief still firmly in place. A moment of madness tempted me again to tear it off, but I didn't. Part of me was terrified of her, she was an unknown quantity, and I wasn't sure how she'd react. I imagined a sharpened stiletto knife secreted somewhere in that voluminous coat.

She grinned, her brows lifting, her eyes wide.

"I'm not armed," she murmured.

I jumped backwards in shock. *She can read my mind!*

"Not all of it, but you broadcast so damn loudly I can hardly think for myself."

I tried a different subject not willing to address that unbelievable statement.

"You know about the tree?" I asked. She nodded. "How long have you known?"

"I knew Alfred." That simple statement floored me. I sat down on the grass at her feet. Thankfully it was dry. This was way too much information to take in standing up.

"My grandfather. You knew my grandfather? But that's impossible."

"I said so, didn't I?"

"Yes, but you're no more than twenty-five years old, at the most."

"No buts. I have work to do. You left here ten years ago, and she is so sad and lonely."

"She?"

"Yes she, your grandmother Lily."

"Now I know you're either lying or mad. My grandmother disappeared before I was born when my mother Sophie was just a child. No one ever found her."

"Correct, all except Alfred."

"I don't understand any of this."

"You're not supposed to, and you're not supposed to be here. Why did you follow me?"

"I told you, I own the estate. My grandfather left the house and the garden to me in his will." She turned from me and surveyed the house and garden like a real estate salesperson assessing value.

"I can see he thought you would care for it better, but you let him down. You haven't been here for years."

"No."

"Wherever you've been I hope it was worth it."

My head slumped to my chest as the feeling of utter failure swamped my heart, tears lurching into my eyes. "I thought it was," I mumbled, unable to hold her gaze.

I didn't notice her moving till I felt her hand touch the back of mine. It was warm and soft and strangely, it tingled with electricity. I looked up into her intent eyes. "She died?"

"Yes. In childbirth two years ago." A pause. "Both of them." Saying the words out loud made my heart twist in my chest and it suddenly became hard to draw in breath.

"I'm sorry." She placed her palm on my chest. That intimate move seemed to ease the pain slightly.

"Thank you." Another pause.

"Now we need to work."

I did a double take. *Did she just say that? I open my soul to a stranger and now she says, get to work?*

"Look, I know you're grieving, but if I don't do something now, this fig tree will be rescinded permanently. I don't want that. You don't want that either."

"Don't I?"

"No. I'm going to take off my kerchief in a moment. Try not to freak out, okay?"

*At bloody last.*

"I mean it. You having a meltdown is not going to help Lily."

*Lily!* I'd forgotten all about my grandmother. *Is what she says true? And if it is, is Lily in danger? If there's any way to save my only relative in the world regardless of how nutty it sounds...*

"Okay I'll try," I mumbled.

Hearing the truth of my words, she turned her back to me and stood facing the tree spreading her arms wide.

"My name is Briony." Once more she'd pre-empted my question. The kerchief lay discarded on the grass, her face turned away from me. *When did she remove that?* I moved. My curiosity getting the better of me.

"Stay still," she admonished. "I have work to do and I can't do it if I'm distracted."

*I can't believe it! Her fingers are growing longer. I must be imagining this. Maybe grief is consuming me?* I shook my head to clear it. It didn't help. Her fingers reached into the bark becoming all brown and gnarly like the tree. Where they met, the air shimmered and her fingers disappeared. *They just bloody vanished!*

"What are you doing?" My voice came out higher than expected.

"Saving your grandmother while I can."

"That can't be my grandmother. Wherever she went, she'd be dead by now."

"Unless she's not." Briony didn't turn to me and her voice sounded strained.

"You okay?"

"Yes, now just stop asking me silly questions. I've nearly got this."

The fig tree seemed to respond to whatever Briony was doing with her hands. The skin in contact with the bark looked like it had merged with it. Buds appeared on the branches, then flowers, then figs.

"Holy shit, you made it flower! It's not due to flower for weeks."

"To use your own quaint words, no shit!" she answered.

Unable to hold back any longer, I stomped around to face this paradox of a woman. Briony's eyes were closed in an expression of concentration. There was sweat across her forehead and running down the side of her left temple. Her blonde hair was stuck to her skin in places and... she was absolutely exquisite. An angel fallen to Earth couldn't have looked more stunning, more ethereal. *Except angels don't swear. Not that I know of. Not that I've met an angel before.* A smile ghosted my face. How long had it been since I smiled?

Briony must have read my thoughts because she opened her deep blue eyes and smiled. I took a breath of stunned surprise at her mouth, displaying a vista of sharp pointed teeth.

"What the...!" I fell flat on my bottom at her feet for a second time. Her grin widened, those extraordinary teeth dominating her angelic face. It was like heaven and hell in one package.

"Like what you see?" she asked tartly. I swallowed hard, too awed and horrified to respond. She clasped her now normal hands together.

"What did you do?" I queried, too frightened to face the proverbial elephant in the room.

"I stabilised her. Lily. She's working properly again." That got my attention.

"Working again. Is she equipment?"

"Sort of." She paused. I deduced she was trying to figure out what more I could handle. Briony sighed, wiping the back of one hand across her damp forehead.

"I guess if you're the house owner, it might be better if you did know."

"Know? Know what?"

"I'm coming to that. Gosh. Are you always so pushy?" I watched slightly disappointed as Briony replaced her kerchief. Although her dental arrangement had freaked me out, it didn't

93

detract from her beauty. *I could look at her all day long.* Briony smiled again.

"Is that so?"

"Stop checking out my thoughts."

"Like I said its difficult when you broadcast so loud."

"I do not." *But she is gorgeous.* Pause. She smiled again. "Drat."

"Want to know about Lily or not?"

"Please."

As Briony took my hand, electricity sang between our fingers. She pulled me to stand and moved us to the back porch where we sat. I scrutinized the fruiting fig tree with trepidation.

"Lily is one of us, one of me in fact. She fell in love with a human, your grandfather, Alfred. The price for that love was to lose her immortality for a period of time, and to offer service indefinitely. Once her time was up, she gave herself willingly to service, on one condition, that she stayed near her beloved family. Lily is now, and forever will be, a portal."

"A portal? Is that like a doorway?" Briony nodded. "To where?"

"Can't tell you that."

"Really?"

"Nope. Otherwise I'd be in Lily's place." We sat a few minutes in silence while I absorbed that information.

"Time for me to go," declared Briony, rising swiftly to her feet. She wiped both hands down her coat, which she still wore, as if to wash away her task, a job completed.

"You're going the wrong way," I called, as she stepped off the porch.

"No, I'm not."

"Your bike's out the front."

I watched enthralled as the woman I'd met by accident only a couple of hours ago, glided closer to the fig tree—towards Lily. Holding onto a branch with one hand, she turned and held out her other arm, palm open, fingers stretched towards me.

"Coming?"

I had nothing left in this world that mattered to me. My wife and child were gone, I was the last remaining member of my family. *I'm actually doing this.*

94

Taking Briony's hand, I let her pull me into an unknown future.

* * * * *

One fig dropped heavily to the ground. On the grass it started to swell. Through the night, it grew, hour by hour, until by dawn it was the size of an adult human male curled in the foetal position.

I woke naked on the grass next to the fig tree planted by my grandfather. It had happened to me several times before, and I'd stopped questioning how I ended up outside each time. My doctor had told me that despite my vivid dreams of a distant place, it was some type of seizure. I accepted his explanation, though it didn't explain why I always woke naked on the grass.

Re-entering the house, I dressed in clothes I kept in a downstairs cupboard, then went to my study where I'd been putting my late grandfather's affairs in order. I was named Alfred after him but preferred to be called Fred by my wife—Lily. He had built the house in the 17th Century and it was my family's inheritance. Sophie was playing with her dolls in her bedroom.

"Have you seen your mother yet?" I asked, as I passed her room. She shook her head, a wry smile displaying a fleeting glimpse of her unusual, pointed teeth. My wife assured me it was a common genetic feature within her family, and we could arrange to have them covered with caps when she was older. I left my daughter, intent on her play, she was used to her mother's comings and goings. Lily had been missing two days now. She sometimes disappeared for a few hours, but not often overnight. I wasn't worried yet, I knew she'd come back to me somehow.

She always did.

# Into The Blue

## By Anne Sikora Lord

I T'S hard to get someone's attention when you can't speak, and they can't hear you. At depth, under water, at night, with a current dragging the opposite way to where I wanted to go, and facing a danger that apparently none of the other descending divers had noticed, I frantically waved my arms. I tried to swim towards Sam, my dive buddy; the current at the edge of the coral reef pushed me back, swirling me around like a lone towel in a washing machine. I kicked hard with my fins, tried to straighten myself. As I frantically powered towards him he caught sight of me, waved, and did the 'okay' sign with his thumb and fingertip. He was oblivious and it was too late...

At the end of our third day aboard the 'Sea Witch', our Mauritian guide had asked if we fancied a night dive. My heart flipped. I was still a relative novice; most of my diving experience was inland water or swimming pools. Even the Red Sea trips were not the exotic turbulent conditions of the Indian Ocean. My expression must have given me away.

"There's nothing to be afraid of missus," he claimed. "Same as day, but torches instead of sun to light our way." His wide, white, toothy smile did not convince me. I had already seen many of the fascinating, but somewhat alarming, creatures of the deep during daylight. A creeping octopus, chameleon-like, swapping colours, blending in as it rapidly but smoothly made its way across the changing rocks and sand of the seabed. Glutinous jellyfish had hung above me, swaying gracefully just below the surface, all frills and tendrils dancing their own ballet. Fabulously exotic lion fish splaying their deadly spines, a fluttering fan gliding towards me. A brief encounter, where a whip-tailed thresher shark off the coast of Egypt, curious about our dive group, silently approached me out of nowhere. It spun away as quickly as it had arrived, but my heart had still pumped a few extra beats. Scuba diving had captured me from my first plunge into the deep, especially the intensely saturated colours of the sea life and its diverse environment. Descending in daylight I was transfixed by how colours are gradually lost, and each time I drifted down I would watch them disappear in the same order that they appear in the rainbow. First to go is red around six metres, followed by orange at fifteen. Yellow disappears about thirty metres, green staying longer and blue the longest. In clear water things look bluer the deeper you go, but at night the sea is a dark and eerie blue-black.

Despite Sam, my dive buddy being a handsome thirty-something, and a highly qualified army diver, I still wasn't sure if I had the courage for a night dive. Tattooed sharks, and other sea-life rippled around his well-muscled arms and would come to life each time he flexed his biceps. These inked works of art fascinated me. I almost felt sorry for him being buddy to a grandma in her late fifties who had a crazy late-life urge to learn something new. But, I knew that my dive master had paired me with him for a reason, and I trusted his judgement implicitly.

"You up for it then?" He grinned, picking up on my pinched face. I shrugged indifferently, not wanting to appear a wimp. When I first met Sam, I had found him to be reserved, quietly watching, an occasional smile tipping a corner of his mouth. I knew he had served in Middle Eastern wars; someone even told me he had a medal for bravery. But at the end of a morning session, another side of his personality would show through. He would fearlessly dive-bomb from the boat rails, acting like a kid with the rest of our group. The youngsters clearly idolised him. I preferred his more circumspect side, where he would patiently instruct me, and offer tips or nuggets of information to help me improve.

"Look, I know you're cautious," he acknowledged. "But you can do it. You've passed all the exams, you have enough experience." I nodded. It was true, I had reached an advanced level in theory and practice—I just needed to keep reminding myself of that.

"And," he added, "despite being an oldie," he nudged my ribs mockingly, "you've got a medical certificate to prove you're fit for purpose, to keep up with a strapper like me."

"Less of the oldie, if you don't mind." I punched his arm.

"You're more capable than you think you are."

"If you dare let go of my hand I will have to kill you." I frowned. He laughed. "I'm serious Sam!"

"Don't worry," he assured me. "I won't."

But he did! As soon as he saw me gaining confidence he released his grip. He stayed close by as we, stage by stage, let the air out of our buoyancy devices, drifting down, checking dials, glancing at our wrist computers, and equalising ear pressure as we went. The sudden current had a different idea, and we were quickly swept apart.

At first, I was confused in the darkness, trying to adjust my eyes amid the sporadic torchlight. Directly below me, as if coming up from the base of the reef wall, was a huge silver creature. All I could make out was a dome shape, curved like the back of a whale. It was rising, slowly. Closing in, it seemed to grow, expanding lengthways—a huge monster of the deep. Fear mixed with excitement as I became transfixed by what I saw. It continued to loom large, close, closer. Gleaming, shimmering, ascending, hugging the reef wall. Something visceral and fearful crept down my spine, confidence fading fast.

It was going to hit me, all of us, disperse us into the deep dark unforgiving water. In my head I screamed. Realising I was holding my breath, I gasped, drawing in a lungful of air and coughing out swallowed water, trying not to choke.

Sam appeared alongside me, grabbing my wrist. My eyes wide, skin pale, the increasing uncontrolled discharge of bubbles—all signs of panic. He signalled to me with his free hand. *Breathe. In... Out... In... Out.* Slowly, slower, reducing my grasping intakes of air, calming me down.

But the beast was still below us, rising, rising.

I pointed down with my free hand. He shook his head. No! He thought I wanted to go deeper, down. He flattened his hand moving it side to side—signalling *level off.*

And then he saw it too. Closing in on us, seemingly metres away, reflecting ominously in our powerful torch beams. There was nowhere to go, no way of avoiding it, whatever it was. The sheer size and power of it. Visions of huge sharp teeth entered my mind. How could I get away? Rapid ascent would cause serious physical damage, if not death. I prepared to kick sideways, thrash at the incandescent glow beneath me.

In a burst it was gone, the effect like a smashed glitter-ball at a disco. I almost choked again with relief.

The monster was now a silver spiral of baby barracuda. Hundreds, if not thousands, of fish in a frenzied cycling shoal. Round and round they went, breaking away, reforming. Luminescent in torchlight, shimmering, flipping and flashing as they turned, gathering together, moving apart in different directions for moments and circling again, reconfiguring into a perfect spiral of inflorescence—breathtaking. Literally.

I could not see his smile hidden behind the demand valve of his regulator, but Sam's eyes, framed by his mask, were crinkled. He was laughing at me. The barracudas had imitated a creature much bigger than themselves to ward off their own predators.

Thirty minutes later, climbing back aboard our waiting boat, I released my demand valve, letting it drop away, and drew in the fresh salty night air.

"Wasn't too bad, was it?" Sam sidled alongside me as we dismantled and rinsed our kit.

"I don't know why I was ever scared," I said, waddling like a penguin as I struggled with my air tank, stowing it alongside the other empties.

"It's about controlling your fear. Mind over matter," he continued, repacking his dive bag as he talked. "You know what you're doing—I'm proud of you for how you coped down there."

"Thanks Sam," I responded shyly. "You don't know how much I appreciate you saying that."

"Even though we both nearly wet our pants?" he asked, pulling a face. We giggled like naughty teenagers.

"Yep. You're my hero." I gave him a grandmotherly hug.

Dive completed, I filled in my logbook—depth reached, air left in tank and of course an account of the imaginary whale-like creature the young barracudas had managed to create. Like a newbie, I wanted to tell everyone what I had seen, but left it there recorded in my logbook. Sam kept his own counsel but directed a cheeky wink at me. Maybe the next dive would bring a real whale sighting. I couldn't wait!

# LATE FOR WORK

## BY ANNE SIKORA LORD

"OH, COME on, come on. Answer please."

[Click]

*Oh God, not the answer machine!*

"Masters, Allchins, and Dreerling, Notaries at Law. Jodie speaking. How can I help?"

*It would be that overpaid young minx answering.*

"Hi Jodie, dear, please could you leave a message for the boss?"

[Audible tut]

*Don't you tut me, missy.*

"I'm sorry, but—I'm running late."

*I really didn't want to get up!*

"Couldn't be helped… "

*I really shouldn't have turned over.*

"First, the alarm didn't go off."

*Yes, it did—I threw it across the room.*

"Then the kids wouldn't get dressed."

*They would have if they'd found clean clothes, and not dragged dirty stuff out of the laundry basket.*

"Once I'd got them dressed, they wouldn't eat their cereal."

*Really? The damned cat had the last of the milk.*

"The car wouldn't start, and the kids had to push it down the road."

*This much is true—but it should have been serviced months ago.*

"And, just as it got going, we noticed our dog chasing us down the road. So, I had to wait while Wayne took him home."

*Well, it was **a** dog, just not ours.*

"With all this delay, we hit the heavy traffic—nose to tail by the time we got to the school gates—Chelsea tractors blocking every parking space."

*Got nabbed by the deputy head—had to listen to a diatribe on the twins' unacceptable behaviour.*

[Another tut]

*If she tuts one more time I shall scream.*

*In for a penny—in for a pound…*

"Good grief, there's a herd of llamas running across the road!"

*I heard it on the local radio news that some had escaped from the petting zoo—just not on this road. I dare you to report that to the boss!*

"And now, there's been an accident and traffic's tailing back for miles."

*Perhaps I shouldn't have turned round to scream at the kids to 'Shut it!' as I drove to their nursery, then I wouldn't have hit the car in front.*

"Thanks for taking the message. Be with you when I can!"

[Click]

# LOST AT SEA

## BY KAREN INCE

TITANIC waves crashed against the rocks and salty spray stung my skin. I huddled behind the largest boulders, wiping my eyes, giving myself respite from the assault of wind and water. I imposed a moment of patience, a deep breath, a slowing of my heart, before once more peering across the turbulent expanse of heaving surf. The dark shape, tossed on the crests and swallowed in the troughs, was still there. It was too far away to tell whether it was *his* boat, or some other unlucky sailor caught out by the swift change in the weather. I ducked back into my shelter.

I looked out again. Grey sky squeezed down on grey sea in an unbroken line. Maybe the boat was hidden by the towering waves closer to shore. I forced my eyes wider open against the attacking spray. Even with the gale propelling it, the boat could not have sailed out of view so fast. If I was sure it was him, I would still gladly have raced the length of the beach, through the wind and rain and driving salt water, to meet him on the quay as usual. Maybe that boat hadn't been his. Salt water leaked from my eyes, blended with sea spray on my cheeks.

I clambered onto the rock to see further, to squint into the squall, to give movement to my body in lieu of hope. Storm winds blew time into the irretrievable past. I shivered in my sodden clothes. Darkness came but his boat did not.

Home gave shelter from the weather but not from my thoughts. With closed eyes I pictured the sea, calm and blue, the sturdy craft gliding through gentle waves to safe harbour. I conjured up his footfall on the stairs. Much later, in my storm-tossed sleep, I dreamt of his strong arms cradling me, salt-laden lips kissing me.

Morning brought sun, and hope. Word might yet come of safe harbour found elsewhere along the rocky coast. I might still run barefoot along the summer beach to meet him on the quay. He might still smile softly at me in the warm winter firelight.

The tide rose and brought me hope of fair sailing. The tide receded and took hope with her. From my window I watched the sea below me.

I never again ran the length of the beach, scrambling over rocks, slipping on seaweed to race his boat to its mooring.

## MULES

### BY KAREN HUTCHINSON

A WAIL of desperation ends the night's silence. I'm on my feet. In the complex? The back gardens? The woods? How close?

Another scream follows. Outside. In the woods.

I pick up one of the sharpest knives I have left. I'm down to my last three. It's supposed to be a lucky number. I started out with thirteen, so who's to say what's lucky?

A fortnight ago, we found the wee lad hidden under a heap of leaves. He'd been covered with a mosaic of wet mosses. Pristine. Not a mark on him. We didn't expect to find him intact. Not after his reed-thin scream petered out. Scared to death. Wasn't meant to happen to an innocent. The others he'd seized had age on their side, supposed to have sense too. Knew better than to be out after sundown.

One by one, floodlights over the back doors whiten the gardens of the housing complex. Squares of yellow light begin to spill from the windows as the residents re-check the metal bars across them. They'll check the bars across their doors too. But they're not going out to help.

My house remains dark. I enter my basement. Slip into the makeshift tunnel under my garden. I had an inkling I'd need an escape route not long after I got stationed here. Discovered the tests weren't sanctioned. Saw what they subjected those men to. I've got traps set in the tunnel to prevent anyone from gaining access to my home.

In the fresher air, under the vast night sky, I crouch inside a low run of shrubs. Stir up the leaf-mould to mask my scent. Past the reach of the floodlights, there's a deepening dark on the horizon. Half a moon, clear sky. Perfect hunting conditions. The temperature's dropped. Adrenaline keeps me warm, alert.

From my left, comes the solid sound of booted heels thumping into the ground, trying to gain purchase. A body being dragged over grass, resisting. Muffled cries. Muffled pain. I can't tell if it's male or female. Animal paths—deer, badger, fox—fan out in front of me. I follow the one that heads towards the crescendo of thrashing, resisting, mounting fear. Known sounds. From his second capture, we've re-lived them, agonised over them. We know the end result.

I hunker, knife in front, point up. Easier to stab upwards, less chance of it being knocked from my grip.

Heavy footsteps to my rear. Too loud. Too close.

I roll off the path. Sink close to the ground. Freeze. Shallow breaths, eyes half-closed. Alert. Heart drumming against my chest.

"Have you got eyes on him?"

"Too fast. Which direction did he go?"

Two young males. Aftershave. Tobacco. Chewing gum. Easy locators. Their confidence will get them killed. Moonlight shimmers on the rifle barrel. Shines along an axe head. Long reach weapons; easy to wrench aside. He's all about an up-close-and-personal assault. Likes to look them in the eyes. Let them see their doom. Newcomers. They exude excitement, adds to their masculine scent. Catnip.

"He's gotta be at the kill site. You ready?"

"Locked and loaded. He won't know what's hit him!" A high-pitched giggle ends this foolish statement.

They run past me; in a crouch, weapons not held up in front. Stupid, but a distraction nevertheless.

I follow them on a parallel line. Match them stride for stride, but mine is softer, masked in their heavy wake.

The axe blade swooshes, cutting the air. Its downward swoosh cleaves not flesh and bone, but dirt, whacking into the ground. A miss. A hollow oomph follows. A gut punch, then another. A rifle blasts. Bullets whine overhead. I keep low; keep heading to the kill site. Behind me, there's a yelp of surprise; the cracking-crunch of a big bone shattering. A voice pleads, "Kill this mother–"

Hysterical man-screams; god-awful sounds of youthful expectations meeting a god-forsaken reality: their death, meted out slow and precise.

I use the escalating noises for cover as I ease to the ground, knifepoint up. Mouth dry. Making sure the noises continue. Making sure he's not using their screams for mercy to creep up behind me. Add me to the menu.

At the kill site fresh blood-scent dampens the air.

The human body holds nine pints, minimum. Blood mist, blood spatter, congealed blood, puddles of it; it's all we've found after each killing, with one exception. The wee boy. Didn't squeeze every droplet of blood out of him.

Blood slicks the grass and I stumble.

The owner of the wail is propped against a tree, gagged, hobbled. Head high, she listens to her rescuers plead for their lives. For an end to their misery. The grunts will receive no special privileges for inexperience. Death will not be swift. I sneak up behind her. She jolts when I tap her shoulder. I muffle her scream. Whisper, "Not a sound. I'm gonna get you out of here." Her arms are tied behind her. I leave the gag in. She's a screamer. If I'm wrong, I don't care. I cut the rope hobbling her ankles and she's up and running, crouched low, beside me, my hand under her armpit to steady her. I can't take a chance she'll stumble. Give our position away. I want him focused on what he's doing. Silence will keep us alive.

Behind us the snarls grow exuberant. She stiffens, makes a low mewling sound.

Underlying the rending of flesh and bone is the hunter's giddy laughter, the odd bellow of delight before the wet chewing, ripping, crunching starts over.

We call it *the feasting*.

Right from his second kill, his noises had infiltrated our homes, lingered long afterwards in our minds, as we listened in aghast silence.

He devours people.

Eats their bones, skin, entrails. Everything, except the blood. It's as if he takes to the treetops, with the body in tow, and wrings it dry. We find blood at his kill site, on the ground, on the trees, on the leaves high above.

She's huffing and puffing through the gag; too much noise. I sense he knows I've rescued her. I match her pace for pace, steer her towards the tunnel. Disable the first set of traps. Once we're in, I reset them to stop him pursuing me inside.

The two men scream in tandem at the man who once was human, to stop. We're immune to it now. She's not. She's straining for air through the gag, hyperventilating. Her eyes wide with panic they're almost all white.

As a final measure I set off my last smoke-bomb behind us in the tunnel. Slide the bolts shut on the steel basement door. In the dark, I guide her upstairs to the kitchen. What drove her to keep on going peters out when we get there. She's out for the count on the floor, half-curled up. I untie her bloodied wrists, ease her onto her back, put a cushion under her head. She's not from here. Different clothes, well fed. Under the gag there's a superficial cut running across her cheek. It'll leave a scar. A reminder. A rib pokes out from a deeper cut. It made her wail. Must have hurt to run, hunched over, and not a squeal from her despite the gag. Better hurting, alive and breathing, than tortured.

I sedated her to stitch her side and wrapped a tight bandage around her ribs. Searched her too. Got a card in her wallet, Ms Lucy

Stock. That's all. Other than her foolhardiness not to carry a weapon.

"Where are you from?" I ask, when she finally comes round.

"Up north. I've been briefed about this facility. Notified the forty test subjects reacted badly to the last... Were put into comas but they flat-lined." She winces as she remembers. "Except for him."

Either the government or the lab-tech rats dispatched her here. My money's on the rats. Failure never was an option for them.

"They can stabilise him with a new vaccine. But they need..."

I laugh. It feels good. An ironic laugh is better than zilch. "You've been suckered. Bosses sent in a bunch of clod-hopping clowns to round him up. A small team of disposables and a decoy. That's you, if you didn't know it. Besides those two, how many more out there?"

She pretends ignorance, but her eyes water. "Eight. I wasn't a decoy."

I snort. "You sure? Where's your partner, your back-up?" It's dawning on her I might be right. "What did the teams bring? Tasers? Tranqs? Plastic bullets? All of the above?"

She slides me a look. Nods. I'm guessing they have other surprises in their arsenal. They need him breathing, aware, undamaged for the most part. Can't plan for stupid.

He'd have expected this. Run each move and counter move every which way. Be ten steps ahead of them—way before they left her as bait. The lab experiments enhanced his tactical abilities. Made him quick-fire smart. The only reason he's stayed around the facility, is us, the people responsible for turning him into a monster.

"Think about what happened out there. He cut you, twice. You screamed. That drew those two squaddies towards you. Doing just what he expected. And he's put on a real good performance tonight. Killing them slow. Theatrics, all of it. He wanted everybody to hear them, not just those of us hiding in here. Are you getting the picture? Your teams are hunkered down, waiting to be picked off. He's off scouting for the bosses who set this mess in play. One piece of advice. Wait until it's light to contact your group. He's gonna keep them pinned down 'til then."

"Won't matter. Techies mentioned micro trackers, too small for him to notice. They'll have eyes all over him by now. They'll know his position. At daylight, they'll send in the back-up teams to capture him wherever he's holed up, asleep. Command centre's set up five miles outside the facility's perimeter."

I can't help myself. I laugh, the second time in as many hours. It feels good. Normal. "You're gonna tell me they're at the farm, right?"

My face must be a book as she's reading my thoughts.

"Oh, no."

I nod, hold back any hope this nightmare will be over soon. "Farm is his HQ. He keeps an eye on us from there. With all the surveillance equipment, back-up generators, and computers, he's been waiting for this. Thought you guys were supposed to be smart." I stop with the doom-talk. She's upset and hurting. She's grasped the situation. "Wait until sun up. He'll hide out. You can regroup with what's left of your *team*."

I envy her. She's sound asleep on the couch. No one here sleeps that deeply.

Nine months ago, he broke out of the lab. His mind hard-wired by a computer. His faculties enhanced to the nth degree. Ravenous, craving. I could tag on enraged, confused, lonely—but deep down he's an alpha predator and we're it. His food supply. The day he escaped, he stormed into the residences. Searching each one until he came to Mike's. Head honcho. In charge of the whole shebang. He grabbed Mike, lifted him off his feet and rattled him unconscious. Hauled him out through the window, across the back lawns. Set him down at the perimeter of the woods. A bunch of us traipsed after them not sure what we were going to do. Mags, the second-in-command, tried to reason with him. Ordered him to let Mike go.

A feral grin distorted his face.

A split second. A nano second. My guts churned in freefall. I wanted out of there but my feet refused me.

He stared at Mags. His jaw opened, wider and wider, and he munched down on Mike's neck. Gripped Mike's arm and tore it clean off. Dropped it at Mike's feet. Still keeping eye contact with Mags, he crunched through Mike's spine. Slurped marrow off his chin. The instant he looked away, we ran. Barricaded our homes.

107

Since then, he's hunted anyone stupid enough to venture out at sundown. They scream for mercy. Beg to be rescued.

Happened once only. A foolhardy individual. Took the only gun we had. Lent him bravado, I expect. Shots fired. One after the other. Emptied the gun. We held our breath. Hoped. Until a duet of screams rang out. He toyed with them. They screamed until daybreak.

By my count we're down to fifteen adults, four teenagers, and two children. The wee boy's sisters.

We're in the middle of nowhere. Miles from civilisation. Sixty minutes after he escaped all communications went down. None of our vehicles work. He ripped out the transmissions. He's got us boxed in. Waiting for the cavalry. He's left us with electricity in the residences but disconnected us from the gas mains. Our food's running out. I hunt from ten in the morning to three in the afternoon. Trap what I can. Most times, he destroys my traps and snares, to weaken us further.

We waited to be rescued. Tonight, the rescue team turned up. To capture him.

Dawn breaks. There are heavy boots on the ground. The newcomers are all grins and fist pumping. Word is they got him. We won't believe he's dead until we see his corpse. Got to hand it to the scumbag lab rats and the bosses. They out-manoeuvred him. Thought one step ahead of him.

Who'd have believed they'd send in suicide squads? There were enough sedatives inside two men to take down an elephant. He devoured the capsules they'd swallowed, chomped down the sedatives, ate the trackers too.

Up at the farm, they'd followed his position on their screens. Saw him stop. Stay stopped. Certain they had him.

They replay the video for us. It shows the team at the farm punching the air; the sound of their whoops come over loud and clear. Joyful. Back clapping. Wide grins.

The video feed cuts out, becomes a blue pinprick on a darkening screen.

Later, they showed us black and white photographs taken at the farm. The room festooned with ripped off arms and legs; torsos lent against the walls. He'd stacked the heads in a pyramid. Faces looking out. Never took one bite.

No need.

They found him. Head down, legs crossed, at rest. His feet set on top of the pyramid. He'd *feasted* on four of the first team. In his open palm lay four trackers. Ate one man too many, they said. An error on their part.

Not his.

# RIVER LIFE

## BY KAREN INCE

ANYA and Dari were at the river fetching water, catching fish. The river supported them, their family, their village. Dari was up to his waist in water, while Anya sat on the bank watching him, and placing the fish he threw to her into a small woven basket. They had filled the water pots before he stepped into the water, stirring up the mud, turning the clear water cloudy. Sudden swirls of movement in the murky fluid behind Dari caught Anya's eye. She froze. The fish in her hands wriggled free, flopped onto the bank, slid unnoticed into the water. Fat sapphire-blue tentacles surfaced and encircled his face, neck and chest. The multitude of paler blue suckers fastened onto his skin, distorting his features, tearing at him like velcro as he writhed.

Hours later her parents found her still sitting in the same place. They asked where Dari was. She pointed at the water. When they asked if Dari was dead, she nodded. The family mourned. The village mourned. The elders questioned Anya, but she did not speak.

Five days passed then Anya went alone to the river. One by one she dropped petals from a forget-me-not into the water. With each petal she recalled a memory of her beloved brother.

When darkness fell that night, Dari arrived at the door, wet, shivering, draped in weeds. The family rejoiced. Anya did not speak.

After a week Anya again went alone to the river. She sat in a tree, high above the water, watching. Dari came, looking around, not walking directly to the river, but getting closer in a series of sideways moves like the knight on a chessboard. He checked again that no-one was there. He removed his clothes, and Anya saw circular marks all over his body. He slipped into the water, and tentacles began to grow from the circles. His arms and legs transformed. He dived under the water and surfaced some distance away. Anya watched as it played in the water and ate the fish it caught in its supple blue tentacles.

The creature climbed out of the river, its blue skin covered with lighter-coloured suckers. As it dried in the heat of the sun, the suckers faded, the blue blended into his normal light brown skin. Dari dressed and returned to the village.

As day gently sank into evening, Anya returned home. She did not speak.

## THE GARDEN

### BY SHIRALEE MATTHEWS

INNOCENT spring daffodils
  fold to spicy bluebells,
Spiky globe thistles
  take hard-won corners from stately delphiniums,
And bearded irises look on
  watching sly periwinkle creep to conquer.

# THE GUEST HOUSE SAGA

## BY MARY GUMSLEY

L ET me introduce myself; I am Eve Armstrong, and I used to run a boarding house in an unfashionable part of London called West Hampstead, until I retired four years ago. My friends and family call me Aunty Eve. I inherited my parents' house, a well-loved Victorian home, with imposing turrets and an elegant balcony which was framed by intricate, lacy iron railings. From street level, the railings served to hide the reality that the balcony was unsafe, but from inside one could see through the worn wooden boarding.

There was a rumour that the previous owner had fallen through those flaking boards into the cotoneaster shrubbery underneath. Cotoneaster is a useful shrub that covers ugly walls and unattractive parts of the garden most people want to conceal. However, it has vicious branches that can cause a serious injury. When the gentleman finally emerged, he was traumatized by this unsettling experience, and covered in red berry juice, which looked like blood. He also had severe cuts from those needle-like cotoneaster branches. He never repaired the balcony after that, and sadly neither did I. The reason for this was I thought it wiser to keep my boarders away from the balcony area, and I kept the entrance door locked.

I loved my sliding sash windows. I enjoyed having two horizontal windows that I could move up and down seamlessly. They gave such an airy feel to the house, and though it cost me a lot to maintain them, I always said it was worth it.

I kept the beautiful black iron fireplaces too, even the ones in the lodgers' rooms, despite the necessity to install central heating later. I enjoyed keeping the biggest fireplace in the lounge, a reminder of the days when we had real log fires, and we would sit and warm ourselves on cold days in winter. Those leaping red flames were comforting, and along with the Christmas decorations gave a feeling of happiness and togetherness. Every year I made a luxurious swag from the branches of holly and ivy trees in the garden, to transform the cool marble mantelpiece into a Christmas showstopper. The antique cuckoo clock remained a permanent feature above the fireplace, its very presence another reminder of happy days in years gone by. I continued the practice of hanging knitted stockings on the fireplace for Father Christmas to fill. Those stockings amused my lodgers who knew I didn't have children. I told them everyone has a place for nostalgia in their lives.

Apart from my house, my pride and joy was my beautiful kist. A kist is basically a storage chest, and many people kept the best specimens as heirlooms. Mine fell into this category. It was made from walnut, and had a domed lid, which was decorated with Tudor roses. Around the edge was a Fleur De Lys design, giving it a medieval look, although I didn't know the age of the chest. It had a lock which was broken so I installed a metal hasp and attached a padlock. It got the nickname of Aunty Eve's Kist, and I was happy about that, it bestowed a comforting familiarity to me.

A kist has to be more than a storage for linen, it has to have some secrets, so I made sure that when people admired it, they were not allowed to look inside. When they looked closer, it became obvious that there was a combination lock. No one could resist asking the inevitable question, "What does your kist contain?"

My cryptic reply was as short as possible. "Just odds and ends." No one asked more questions after I gave them that explanation!

Most of my boarders were people from outside London who came to the city for a better life. There were many accountants. In fact, I began to believe that London was mostly inhabited by finance people. They were the quietest tenants, and they paid their rent regularly.

Next were the entrepreneurs, not just people doing party planning or direct sales, but people who opened exciting shops. Over the years, I collected my fair share of what I call 'tat' bought as an act of kindness to encourage them to pay their rent on time. To this day I own Tupperware, soft cuddly toys, Barbie dolls—I meant to give to my nieces—and all sorts of gourmet delights with unmentionable names.

Another group were the entertainers. They were the most creative of the lot, particularly when it came to excuses for not paying their rent. I have to say I liked the singers best—when they could really sing. One young girl had a marvellous soprano voice, and she was so flattered when I told her she sounded like Maria Callas. Most of the boarders had never heard of Maria Callas, because they were too young. I remember her singing an aria from La Bohème in the garden one night, and many of my lodgers leant out of their windows to listen to her. There were people in the street watching and listening too. Free entertainment was much sought after in this part of North London. La Bohème is a sad opera, and her voice expressed all the emotions of the doomed heroine. When she saw me in tears, she realized she had the ability to move an audience.

The actors of course, not to be outdone, would perform in groups and I was often called upon to be what I would euphemistically describe as an 'extra' —just to help them learn their parts. This was a very convenient ploy for me. I'd attach myself to the ones who did not pay, so I kept them in my sights until they paid their rent. As an extra, I played everything from unruly members of a crowd to serial murderers escaping the long arm of the law. Usually, all I had to do was remember a few words.

The last group were the dancers, and these were often flamboyant people who loved to strut around wearing as little as possible showing off their usually enviable physiques. One young chap made such a habit of it, coming down to breakfast wearing little more than a pair of speedos, that I received complaints from many of the lodgers. When I told him of this and mentioned there was a local peeping tom who was known to spy on everybody in the neighbourhood, I thought he would stop. Whilst he refrained from coming down to breakfast in his speedos, he still continued walking round the house scantily clad. I was told he never kept his curtains closed either. He was warned. Some boarders stayed for months, others were resident for years, and they became friends, telling me their problems and sharing their successes. When they left, I sometimes felt a little sad.

I had collected lots of memorabilia over the years. I particularly loved clocks, but my cuckoo clock was the only one I put on display. There were lots of burglaries in West Hampstead, and clocks were a common item stolen. My solution was to put them in the kist. This was my alternative to using a burglar alarm. I suspected that a few of the burglaries which occurred, might have been carried out by my lodgers, many of whom were broke most of the time. I could never prove who the culprits were, but the combination lock proved to be the answer. No one ever discovered it, except for one person, and this is the story I want to share with you.

Amongst my many lodgers was an actor/dancer in his thirties called Jared. His work was unknown to me, but my taste in West End plays was more of the Shakespeare, Miller, Chekhov type, not modern musicals, and whodunits. He was currently 'resting' and was hoping for a part in a revived version of 42$^{nd}$ Street, in the West End. I actually liked 42$^{nd}$ Street and had even seen the 1930's film which marked Ginger Rogers' debut. Like a sensible lad, he was auditioning for all sorts of parts. Meanwhile, as he had to pay his way, he got a position where he performed gorillagrams at parties. Here he would hand out presents and do a dance for drunken girls who'd seen too many versions of the Full Monty.

He did not like having to earn his living this way, but it was work, and he had a girlfriend called Madeleine Evan-Hart who was threatening to finish with him if he did not get a 'proper' position. We often spoke when she came to see Jared. One day, when he was held up at work, I invited her into my lounge, and she, like so many others, admired and commented on my kist.

I guessed she had something on her mind other than the kist. I had often heard her arguing with Jared, and suspected that their relationship was not as harmonious as it appeared. She looked at me tentatively at first, before deciding to open up.

"Aunty Eve, Jared and I are in our thirties. We've been together six years. Nothing has changed. He spends far too much time touring the provinces."

I noticed she couldn't keep her hands still as she spoke, winding her hair around her fingers, her nails ragged and bitten. I sensed by her body language that she was genuinely frustrated.

"I don't see enough of him, and he never seems to get important parts. I'm sure he has talent, but he is always waiting for his big break which never happens. I want out."

With that she banged the side of the chair emphatically, and flopped back, exhausted by her revelations. She was desperate for someone to help her.

I wished I could say something soothing, that the break would come, but she had probably heard that a thousand times before from Jared.

"Madeleine, the West End is too small for all the people who are looking for work there. That is why few people succeed. I know it is hard to understand."

With that she burst into tears, and I found myself fumbling for a tissue to comfort her. She tried to stop her trembling hands and dabbed at her tears, but I could see why she wanted out. Six years would be more than enough for anyone, I reasoned. I was about to go and make her a cup of tea when I heard a knock on the door. It was Jared. He could see she was upset, and he probably knew why, but he avoided the issue and gently took her arm, steering her away. I guessed he wanted to get Madeleine away from me before she revealed more secrets about the two of them.

Time went by and Jared carried on with his gorillagrams and Madeleine looked increasingly unhappy. I could see an imminent break up between the two of them. At heart I felt the same as Madeleine, that he was talented enough to make the big time.

I liked to check my kist occasionally, to make sure no-one in the house had discovered the combination. This was an unlikely event, as although it was something I wanted people to admire, I did not allow many visitors in my lounge.

Imagine my surprise one day when I opened the kist and found a tiny jewellery box sitting on top of my precious clocks. I thought I must be getting senile. Had I put a gift for a friend or relative in there that I had forgotten? Perhaps someone had cracked the combination. Was this something stolen that a thief wished to hide? I checked my clocks. They were all there. My mind was spinning. I imagined it was an expensive stolen ring in there. It could be worth millions, perhaps be part of a heist in the City of London. There had been a lot of heists in London recently. Surely, I reasoned, a thief would want to hide several items not just one expensive ring?

With these questions buzzing in my mind, my curiosity got the better of my manic meandering, and I opened the box. It contained an engagement ring. It was very pretty—a round, vivid blue sapphire surrounded by tiny diamonds. It wasn't a chain store ring, but it wasn't worth millions. I couldn't work out what to do. I

115

couldn't call the police. They rarely came out unless it was for a massive burglary. They would laugh and assume I was a senile old lady if I told them that something had been *added* to my items. I could just imagine the laughter amongst the police officers.

"Got a fairy godmother then, love? Whoever it is, send her to me. Just make sure she's young and pretty."

I decided to call a meeting of the residents. At that time, I had ten lodgers. I would tell them something was missing, and this might enable me to guess who the culprit was. I hoped the guilty party would own up.

Their reactions were a surprise. They were incensed to think that someone had taken one of my belongings. I was very careful not to accuse anyone directly. The two girls who lived on the top floor, looked genuinely upset, shook their heads and kept saying, "No, no, no."

The four boys who lived on the first floor looked aghast, and chimed in chorus, "It definitely wasn't us." They kept looking at each other in disbelief.

Then the last group of girls on the ground floor, who often ran errands for me said, "How could you accuse us when we do so much for you?" They shook their heads.

Jared sat quietly while all this was going on looking as surprised as everyone else. He was an actor, and perhaps he could easily fool me. I looked from one face to another in bewilderment, everyone reacted as if I had suggested something that was preposterous. As no one owned up, I gave an exasperated sigh, and ended the meeting.

After everyone left, I put my head in my hands. There was a breach of security in my house. Who knows, there might actually be things missing and I was not even aware of it. I wondered what to do next.

After about five minutes, I heard a tentative knock on the door. I opened it, and there was Jared, looking very sorry for himself. At first, he couldn't look me in the eye, and then the words came tumbling out, as if he were struggling to say something. Jared was not usually tongue-tied, quite the reverse, in fact. He looked away again, and then opened up.

"I bought the ring ages ago. I didn't want Madeleine to find it. I wanted to wait for my big break before I proposed to her. You know how she notices everything. When I saw your kist, I thought that would be a good place to hide it. I hoped you'd look in there only now and then. Please forgive me, it was a very stupid thing to do. That is your property, and I had no right to go in there, but I was desperate. Please, could I ask that you let me leave it there until I propose?"

I pondered that proposition. I was still bristling with anger, and normally when tenants lost my trust, I just asked them to leave. I bit my lip to stop myself from telling him to do just that. He had owned up and if I had a favourite person, it had to be Jared and my disappointment was the reason I was devastated by his deviousness.

"So how did you find the combination?" He looked me in the eye again.

"I noticed the pantry door hinge was broken and the door was always slightly ajar. I was looking for somewhere to hide the ring. That was how I came to see the small blackboard. I saw that you wrote items you needed to replace on it. There were four numbers written clearly at the bottom that seemed unrelated to everything else. It struck me that this was the combination number. I tried it and it worked. I know you are very cross with me, but I couldn't think of anywhere else to hide it."

I was still cross but was feeling less violated once he offered his defence.

"I am surprised that someone managed to figure it out. I thought it was foolproof," I muttered. He gave an enigmatic smile.

"I am interested in codes and I am incredibly nosey. Can I help you..." he hesitated at this point, not wanting to upset me, I suppose, "...with a more modern way to hide the number." And with that, I decided it was time to embrace 21st century technology and put it on my phone at long last.

Jared got the part he so coveted and got engaged, despite their problematic courtship. The happy couple made plans for the future, and the kist tale became a quirky family story. It was a happy ending for them, and I got to see 42nd Street. Backstage, I told him afterwards he must look for parts in spy sagas in the future. He laughed heartily and I wished him well for the future.

# TWISTED FAITH

## BY TRACEY KATHLEEN JACOBS

**W**EEK **Three of Lockdown**

Dave was making extra noise that morning. The delicious smell of bacon wafted upstairs. Every Sunday, Dave hogged the kitchen to do a cooked breakfast. At some point he'd shout upstairs and offer Jude a sandwich or something. Much to her amazement, that morning he didn't. Well, they were in week three of Lockdown and she'd done nothing but moan at him for the amount he ate, so maybe that's why. She shrugged. *Do I care? Would I really miss a greasy bacon or sausage sandwich this morning? The answer is yes, I would, but I'm not giving in and making the first move. If he wants to share his breakfast with me, he will ask.*

Jude decided to pray. They'd stopped going to church because Dave said it's full of old people and bible-bashers. Jude never pushed him about going back, just went along with his decision, anything for a quiet life. So, she prayed alone. Sometimes she had her doubts and had been known to be quarrelsome about *The Invisible One*, as Dave called him. Then, if she thought she'd got good reason to believe that he works in mysterious ways, (The Lord, that is, not Dave) her faith returned. Oh, come on, we all do this surely?

"Dear Lord. I tr—"

"Jude!" Dave's voice boomed up the stairs. "There anything you want?"

"No, nothing for me, thanks."

118

"I'll do you a bacon sarnie anyway. You chatting to The Invisible One again?" he teased.

Jude sighed. She had clearly said no to a sandwich. He made a habit of interrupting her prayers.

"Dear Lord, I trust only you. Please do not judge me too harshly. Oh, and I have sinned Lord, believe me, I truly have. The thing is, I had my reasons. You'll be disappointed with me, even though I'm sorry. I lied again Lord. I told a big, fat, dirty one. It's changed the situation, like I intended it to. My plan worked Lord, but I'm not too sure if I'm happy about it. Will you guide me? Can you help me to put it right, or at least be brave enough to admit it to him? Can you help me put an end to all this deceit?

"You see Lord, before Lockdown started, I was aware that Dave was acting odd. I'd seen him like this before, so I was suspicious. I know I shouldn't have been judgemental towards him, but I'm very insecure. You know why Lord, of course you do. It's *his* fault. I know you've already heard all of this, so please forgive me for repeating myself.

"As you know Lord, I spied on them. On that afternoon in March, I faked a bad headache and managed to leave work early. It was easy as we'd been quiet because of the Corona scare and some had already left anyway, *including* Kelly Duncan. I'd been aware of her for a few months. But recently she'd changed towards me, not as chatty and friendly. He met her at our office Christmas get together. Kelly Duncan. A slim, pretty, natural blonde. An instant threat to a woman as insecure as me.

"You know the rest, but I'll elaborate anyway Lord. I called in on a dear old friend of my mother's, called Martha. I'd discovered she lived across the road from that bitch Kelly. Her front room window was in the prime position. My previous visits had come to no avail, but this time I saw what I needed to see. Just after five p.m., sure enough, he got out of his—no, sorry—*our* car and went straight into her house. Mission accomplished!

"As it had turned colder outside, Martha never came to the door when I left. This was handy for me as I wanted to take a sneaky photo of our car, without any awkward questions from her. My mind was all over the place as I walked home. Lord, is it odd that I was still giggling about something Martha had told me? It was funny though; she wore kingfisher blue bloomers under her white wedding dress. Nobody had brought her anything blue, so her old bloomers came to the rescue. Even funnier was later that night, when Harry, her new husband, had roared with laughter at the sight of them, calling them 'passion killers'! The mind boggles. Sorry Lord, I rambled on a bit there.

"But how Lord? How could I still be giggling, after proving to myself that he was being unfaithful again? It's because I'm used to it, isn't it? Surely, I should've been sobbing my heart out. Oh well, that's me. Me, who was clever at putting on a happy face, even though I was boiling with rage inside. Somehow, I made it home. I started to prepare dinner, but I had a headache, didn't I? So, I rang Dave to ask if he'd mind having something simple as I wasn't feeling well. Honestly the shame of the man, Lord. He even failed miserably at trying to sound concerned, and said he was about to ring his last client for the day and would be home within the hour. I had to stop myself from screaming abuse at him.

"Lord, you know the rest. He came home, we ate in silence and I seethed inside. He remained oblivious that I knew about his latest fling. Lockdown was official the very next day, and since then we've been stuck in here. Apart from the necessary shopping trips, it's been just us. I've had a lot of time to think about things and put my plan into action.

"I know I'm not perfect, so I can understand why he would get the urge to stray again. As you know Lord, this is one of many times. The first was within a year of us marrying. Her name was Yvette, and I managed to get her to dump him by 'accidentally' letting it slip that he had a gambling problem. He liked the odd flutter, and enough people knew about this, so it was simple to get her to believe me. I'd casually mentioned that we were struggling financially, because of his addiction. Both were unaware that I knew about their dirty little arrangement.

"The second fling was a woman named Patricia. *She* never let anyone shorten her name to Pat or even Patsy. Who the Hell did she think she was anyway? Sorry Lord, I shouldn't say that. 'Hell' isn't a nice word. I've never been sure what happened between them. It ended suddenly, and Patricia was soon with another man. I've yet to find out more about that one. You'll already know all the sordid details.

"Back to Kelly, the *popular* Miss Duncan. Younger, prettier, and slimmer than me. I needed to put him off her too, or vice-versa. I had to think of something. Lord, I know I'm repeating myself again as I've asked you this before, but did I need to be so cruel? Would you prefer me to forgive my husband for his flaws?

"Anyway, the weirdness and loneliness of lockdown made it look normal for me to befriend Kelly. A colleague that needed to chat, seemed fine for the circumstances. For some those few minutes were a life saver. I'd ask the usual things like, 'How are you coping with this lockdown?' or, 'Have you got everything you need?' It was tailor-made as they say. She kept asking about Dave. I expected that; questions like 'How is he doing?' and 'How are you both coping being stuck in all the time?' I put my idea into action. I decided to let him know that I'd become her friend, and that we were planning to meet up when this whole isolation scenario was over. We'd made no such plans, but I wanted to see him squirm.

I saw my chance one evening, whilst we were eating in silence yet again. I mentioned how much we'd been chatting online. How lovely and caring Kelly seemed. I told him I felt like I'd made a *true* friend at last. I said 'She's told me so much about herself and always asks after you too. How considerate.' Well Lord, you already know that he wriggled with embarrassment as he said, 'Yeah but, Kelly's ten years younger than you, best keep her a colleague.' I agreed, but couldn't help adding that, 'I promised I wouldn't tell anyone this, but I know I can trust you. She's been seeing this fit gym instructor who lives across the road from her. He's with her practically twenty-four-seven! So much for social distancing!' I'd laughed as I said that to make it sound more believable. I will never forget the look on his face. I momentarily started to feel sorry for him, but that didn't last long! Forgive me for gloating, but I relished the moment of grim realisation as it dawned on him that he is getting old and is losing his sex appeal. I think my observations were correct. Once again Lord, forgive me for gloating.

"But what am I going to do when we return to work? I've got to face her. That will be awkward. I needed to confess this to you Lord. Do you think I've behaved in an evil manner? As you know

Dave has tolerated my insecurity and paranoia for years; unaware that I secretly blame him. What do I do Lord? I need your guidance. I can't keep him away from her forever, especially when lockdown's over. I'm begging for your help. I need this deceit and misery to end. Thank you.

"I ask this in Jesus' name.

"Amen."

## Week Four of Lockdown

Rain trickles down the bedroom window. It had been a rough night but is much calmer now. Slouched in the same place where Jude prayed exactly a week earlier, is Dave. He begins to pray.

"Dear Lord. God. Our Father. Whatever it is I should call you. You must forgive me. I didn't mean to listen to her prayer. It was wrong. My mother warned me that listeners never hear any good of themselves. But I didn't expect to hear all that. Never in a million years did I realise what Jude was capable of. So many questions answered in a short space of time, things started to make sense. Jude couldn't speak softly, no matter how hard she tried. I never heard it all, but I was halfway up the stairs with her sarnie for Christ's sake—whoops, sorry—but I was. As usual she'd said no, but I knew she really wanted one, so I'd made it anyway.

"I cared about her you know. I stayed with her even though I knew she was 'high maintenance.' A sarnie short of a picnic and all that! I never meant this to happen. I came in here to talk to Jude about it. She went ballistic, screaming and hitting me, and it bloody hurt. She even bit me! She was so loud. I didn't want the neighbours to hear. I tried to silence her.

"Jude was a lot stronger than she looked. She pushed me off and started running for the stairs. The next thing I heard was the sickening thuds as she bounced down them. I swear to you she tripped. I'm never gonna forget the sight of her lying still at the bottom. I reckon she broke her neck falling like that. I should've called an ambulance, but I could tell she'd gone. Jude was clearly dead.

"Instantly I realised that they'd blame me. With good reason. I'd be the main suspect. I know I didn't handle the situation right, but I panicked. All I could think about was where do I put her?

Solution—the basement. She'd hated that dark, dingy place, but what other choice did I have? She was heavier than I thought, but I managed it God. I dragged her down and laid her in there. On her favourite blanket of course! She looks peaceful enough. I caught sight of myself in a cracked mirror that's been stored there. I didn't like who was staring back at me. What kind of man have I become? Seven years bad luck is an understatement compared to what I'm experiencing. Now what? I guess that when this isolation ends, life will become one continuous lie for me. I'm living on borrowed time and desperate for your help.

"Please forgive me—I'm truly sorry.

"Amen."

## WAVES OF THE UNEXPECTED

### BY ANNA SPAIN

THE sun hangs languorously above the horizon and infuses the soporific waves with a golden liquid light. At the end of a hot June day I sit on the shoreline with my book, hugging my knees, knowing that I had made the right decision to move to the coast.

Warmth seeps into my skin, words from the page fill my mind until a shadow falls across the open book. I look up and He stands in front of me, an apparition with long, straight, black hair and hooded eyes that look down, then open wide as bowls of cerulean sea. My reality is lost in a sea mist. I shiver as a thick mineral vapour steams from His body. He is now sitting next to me. Whoa mind, stop cartwheeling across the sand; and tongue, why are you wedged in tight with mad talk that tingles fiercely on my lips?

The candyfloss sunset has become irrelevant. Instead, an ache threads itself under my skin and out to my fingertips that thumb the pages of my book, wishing it were His oiled bronze skin. "Is He real?" I murmur to myself like a gibberish old woman. Three words roll around my tongue and slowly slip out, "Who are you?"

The question, "Who do you think I am?" rumbles back to me.

I look around to make sure no one is within earshot, as I'm sure their eyebrows would rise and mouth twist into a smirk when I reply, "You're a merman."

He tells me about His race, the merfolk, sea people who existed long before we humans arrived. I can imagine their fascination, aeons ago when His ancestors first saw humans and their legs. Apparently, our legs changed their perception of the world—it became indisputable there is life beyond the ocean. Legs to walk, run, skip and disappear into the landmass, into another 'world' that they couldn't see.

I get it, I understand that some wanted to live as 'human-folk'—his words. He says that a specific group of merfolk over many a blue moon did adapt to live on land. I want to ask a hundred questions, but he continues talking.

"Humans have lost their way," He says solemnly, "and are now ruining our world too."

My heart shrank for a few beats of life. I felt ashamed; the collective sticky guilt on my palms, as of course I'm one of the human race. Climate change and the extinction of species almost everyday news, and now Him and His people, faced with a dying sea and disease from pollution, plastic and noise.

It's an ugly truth and it hurts. I stare out to sea, my hands burrow into the wet gritty sand that punishes the tender crevice under my fingernails. His hand reaches into the sand and gently takes hold of mine; His skin feels soft, thick and leathery. As I glance up, He looks deep into my eyes and I fall into another reality, a 3D cinema where waves surround us, then mist into millions of hypnotic droplets. His words reverberate inside my head. "Ellie, I know you can help."

My eyes could be on elastic, knocking together with disbelief; I search myself and think, *How can I help? Can a grain of sand save a school of dolphins?*

He says, "I want to show you our secret sea world, unknown by your race."

Those few words punch a hole in my head and put a picture-book story in its place. Overwhelmed, I stutter something about not wearing the right clothes and there is nowhere to put my phone, keys, other belongings. Stupid, limp excuses. Inside I growl with disquiet, unsure about this surreal moment. I wonder why He chose me. I'm confused about who or what He is. Yes, different, unique, a sea-god, a merman. Can it be true? I look at Him obliquely and marvel at His dusky bronze-rose lips, His large eyelids that hover over a thin crescent of azure blue, that can open as an umbrella that is as wide as the sky. I sense a gentleness, kindness, and sincerity; it glows from under His skin as warm embers and soothes my fear. A desire to swim by His side bubbles and the caution slowly ebbs.

\* \* \* \* \*

The following day I go for my usual early morning swim. At work I'm distracted as my mind darts off into unknown sea-worlds. I sneakily google myths and stories about sea-folk and underwater cities; I need something tangible to believe. Anxious heat pricks my face and my stomach twists as I silently read that the lost city of Atlantis, always considered to be a fable, is rooted in truth. Wow, wow, wow, the fantasy is fact and sealed with red wax. The secret inside of me is like a warm doughnut—delicious, scrumptious and moreish.

\* \* \* \* \*

That evening I return to the beach prepared for the big adventure. He looks out from the sea, backlit by a yellow-white sun haze, and walks out of the sea, slowly. Time freezes as my eyes devour the faerie vision. He gives me a bouquet of exquisite gossamer trumpet flowers that shine like mini rainbows. My breath flows rapidly with excitement; I concentrate on easing the square yellow buttons from the slots on my black and white striped beach dress. It gives me time to think and I wonder how old He is—thirty or one hundred and thirty. I can't tell.

He swims upfront until after a mile or so waits, takes my hand and propels us under where we tread water face-to-face. He cups his hands around his mouth, purses his lips and blows a circle of oxygen and continues to blow until it surrounds my head. I breathe as an angel in a bubble, spooky and exhilarating; we swim side-by-side, twist and turn like fish, agile, fast, downwards. All sense of time and orientation fade, except for my heartbeat, a loud gudump…gudump. The light recedes and fright, like a shapeless inky monster, leaps into my heart. He entwines His fingers tightly with mine; I clutch Him as my underwater lifebuoy.

We swim down into circles of light that illuminate a sea garden; bright colours sway like a live abstract painting with bursts of towering cobalt blue plumes. Mouse sized silver fish with streaks of sulphur yellow dart out then hide.

All too soon He points upwards. Feathery plant tentacles slip away and I shiver as we swim back to the shore. The sun is cut in two and disappearing. I run splish-splash across the ridged sand where water pools; with relief I see that my heaped belongings are still on the beach. My front door key is safe in a pocket sewn into my swimsuit. I throw the thick yellow towel around my body, soft against my tingling salty skin. Despite shivering I can't stop the grin spreading across my face. I skip home, a forty-eight-year-old woman—I don't care if people look and wonder if I'm mad. My hair bounces up and down in time with my exultant heart.

* * * * *

The following evening, He prepares me for a longer dive and explains that it will be different, deeper and closer to where they live. I listen carefully to every word. "A sea sponge over each ear will reduce the sound of the anguished sea creatures. Sanctuaries have been set up but sometimes it's too late to restore good health."

Anticipation is riddled with dark thoughts. Why can't it all be beautiful? For one part of this wonderful planet to thrive, unspoilt? His eyes lock with mine and burrow into my groaning heart.

"Pollution is devastating us, and our health. The gardens and palace grottos, sea antiquities that have been crafted over thousands of years have begun to disintegrate. We cannot die out. Ellie you are more than you think you are. We need your help."

"What am I? How can I help?"

He continues to talk, soft whispers that rouse. "Ellie, blood is thicker than water, the DNA cannot be silenced. Some human-folk have distant merfolk ancestry, it will voice its presence and they will be irresistibly drawn to the sea."

126

I want to ask if I'm one of them. I can't, and instead I look into His eyes seeking confirmation; they open wide as before, like huge bowls of turquoise ocean, my mind and reality plunge in deep, among a school of red-lipped pouting fish, each the size of a dog—white whiskers stand out proud on a purple seal-like nose and orange flippers that belong on a duck. Somehow, I know it's a fish of ancient times that swam in the same watery molecules that touch thousands, millions of people every day. The reverie fades and I'm back to us standing on the beach. I watch His fingers work deftly, aquatic plants woven tight to bind us together around our waists. His deep, mellifluous tone flows not aurally but inside my head. "Scientific human-folk have researched the hominid as man's distant ancestor. It's a blessing for us merfolk as we remain undiscovered and exist only in stories and myths. Today, Ellie, you will glimpse your ancient ancestors."

I look at him, my jaw hinged open in shock. I can't think as we swim swiftly out to sea—the sun turns carnelian red and fills me with a rosy joy.

Deep in the sea He hovers over a mottled white rock; in the gloom it looks like a ghost whale, covered in barnacles, mussels, and thick wavy algae. A dark hole appears and we swim inside. Soft yellow pinpricks of light illuminate the darkness and kink off into the distance, edging arches and domed ceilings. Glowing white shells, the size of my head, line a pathway. The underwater grotto reminds me of a Christmas scene with twinkling lights on a dark winter night. No, something's wrong, there are no fish or plants. My blood thumps with alarm. I'm scared and think of my children; I didn't tell anyone I was doing this.

His words filter into my thoughts. "Here the sea is dead with pollution." I stop swimming. My legs are tired and tears run into my mouth. His strong arm pulls me closer into His chest where I feel His heartbeat that is slow and strong. His voice whispers in my head, "Sorry Ellie. Please do this for us." I hold onto Him, our bodies aligned like dancers and I feel safe until debris floats into sight. With revulsion I try to swish it away—we weave and duck under oily layers. Further into the grotto, bones are scattered across the floor, large piles squished into corners. Fish eyes, vacant, stare indecently in yellow putrid flesh. A faint creepy moan seeps through the sea sponges covering my ears and an echo reverberates around the crumbling bricks, a sound of despair and death. The stench permeates the bubble and causes vomit to rise up from my stomach. I panic and can't breathe; my arms furiously grapple, grasping for air while a knife stabs my lungs. He wraps his body around me, breathes another oxygen bubble around us, and waits for my distress to ease then guides me away from the foretaste of their bleak future.

Beyond are merfolk on sentry duty, their long hair floating out as silken strands. As we approach, their heads bow and their hands clasp His in warm greetings. Bubbles the size of large apples rise in a column; we swim in against the rising oxygenated water. Shiny red fish with Mohican magenta tufts rise past us. We descend through forests that teem with tiny fish that burst into kaleidoscopic colours and gigantic boulders that host brilliant coral gardens.

In the distance is a mystical pink dome. As we approach I see the roof is covered in candy-pink water lilies that sway on stems. Inside are baby merfolk. They play and paddle, fudge coloured skin, tiny hands point at me and giggle. Large blue-green eyes, wide with curiosity under tumbling red curls. They are water cherubs and could be in the paintings of Raphael.

\* \* \* \* \*

I made promises when swimming through the fairy-tale scenes; thinking about it now while back at home, it scares the shit out of me. Why did I say today? I become more frayed as the day wears on, the promise rolls around my stomach as if rolling with a prickle of hedgehogs.

Preparation for the task, the mission, is paramount. I give thought to my clothes and appearance, as I need a confidence boost to walk tall, with style. I plait my long auburn hair in cornbraids, put on a soft-cut, white linen dress and a straw hat. I apply coral coloured lip-gloss and shade my green eyes with sunglasses.

At four p.m. I approach Ramsgate Harbour and stand before the ominous blue criss-cross metal gateway—it towers above me and sticks its rusty fingers up at me as if I've already failed. The cold chunky latch slides to the left, the gate squeaks as a trumpet blast in my ears. I push it and step through to the inner harbour where the

128

boats are moored, then walk down the sloping walkway. My legs no longer feel like flesh and bone, just jelly. At the first yacht a man eyes me suspiciously and asks if I'm a Jehovah's Witness—it must be the leaflet I'm holding in my hand.

"No," I say. "But I am on a mission." I inwardly cringe as I thrust a folded paper sheet at him. Nine words say:

A WORLD UNSEEN WILL BE SEEN BY A FEW

He looks at it and frowns. Questions seem to stack across his tanned, seafaring face. I imagine his thought bubble, 'Lunatic. She's a lunatic.' I urge him to continue reading. He looks again, turns over the page, shrugs and starts to turn away.

"Please, let me." I take the paper from him, breathe on it and words appear.

"Blimey O'Riley, how did that happen?"

"I don't know. It's a prelude." I smile at the kooky magic, and hand it back to him. It reads:

> Visions sweet
> Swell with shells
> Tastes and smells anew.
> Fantastical life is tucked away,
> Far under the sea, in
> Caverns, gardens and grottos,
> Fish-mammals that you won't believe.
> Consider that you are special,
> As you have been chosen to see.

YES OR NO?

I impress upon him that it's not a riddle or a game. I remove my sunglasses and with a big confident smile I say, "It will blow your mind, and if it doesn't I will take you out to dinner."

His green-grey eyes are still, unblinking like a fish—face expressionless until a huge grin lights him up. He said, "It sounds nuts, but hey live and let live, that's my motto." I like this man and I want to hug him. Instead, I fill the air with nervous chatter and polite questions. I learn that Brian is around fifty, down to earth and lived a nautical life. He wears a red canvas cap that tussles with his thick, dark-blonde hair that is determined to pop out as mini haystacks. I intuitively trust Brian and tell him what I've seen under the sea. He takes me to meet Inchy, then Sally, Charlie, Jerry, Monty, Caroline, Jack, Alice, Ben and others that I can't remember; each on their respective boats, some with partners, others alone. Again and again I explain and describe how it started. Brian charms them with an easy-going silvered tongue. We walk and talk our way onto boats and yachts until eleven seafaring people are up for an adventure.

We sail at eight that evening. Nine boats anchor on the Goodwin Sands. A small colony of seals with dark mournful eyes grumpily and languorously roll off into the sea when a large wave brings Him accompanied by eleven merfolk. They pair up with each of us and prepare for the dive.

Out of the blue we are engulfed by a tempest; thunder deafens and lightening flashes across a charcoal sky. Words as if from the belly of the ocean roar, "This mission is sacrosanct. Do not violate our secret, or you will NEVER BE SAFE AT SEA." The merfolk's eyes retract into vivid coloured crescents and the storm subsides. We stand immobile as dummies with trepidation and excitement.

After the final preparation we swim down, escorted, far from the summer evening sky.

Time passes quickly and all too soon we're guided back to a sandbank near the boats and the merfolk leave. Awe and deep thought silence our tongues, the same as when you've watched a mind-blowing film, that has tugged you away from yourself into something more important. Before sailing back we hug one another goodbye, and arrange to meet the following day at Cliffs in Margate.

Delightful images accompany me to bed. Dark and ugly thoughts spiral into my dreams and screw the sheet tightly as I twist restlessly from side to side. I wake to damp folds that reinforce my anguish about privilege and responsibility. To reveal their secret is certain exploitation; commerce would monetise and manipulate the merfolk as an underwater extravaganza. As I step from the bed, words erupt from my mouth, "That will never happen!" The sound fills the quiet room with steadfast certainty.

I think about our voyage back last night. Brian talked about his great, great grandfather, Captain Maurice Comfrey, a seaman from Margate. His boat 'The Black Octopus' sank on the sandbanks off the coast of Deal. It appears that the merfolk have prolific memories. The mermaid who partnered him described it to Brian as, 'Black noise of the storm, nautical-folk shouting and fighting against the mighty waves that tossed the ship as a plaything. Wooden masts creaked, ripped, then lurched into the devouring sea.' We know it was not an uncommon occurrence at the time, but what really surprised Brian was Her memory of Maurice. She spoke of his courage as he helped to save his crew.

Brian has a softness I like, and an emotional openness. "I don't choke up often, but I did when she said that Maurice adapted to an aquatic life, formed a bond and had children. The lucky bugger."

Wow, truly amazing; hybrid children, half human, half merfolk. It must be the oxygen bubble that allowed him to live—or is it just a story, a myth?

As I walk to the café I contemplate their trust in us. We know their true selves, not murderous brutes or flirting siren lusting for death; beautiful sea people that are peaceable, kind and gifted.

Inchy comes rushing into the café at eleven a.m. Cheeks flushed red with anxiety, he sits down, panicked words shoot out. "Sally has disappeared. Her boat has gone." We look at one another in stony silence and fear the worst.

Under the pressing hush I try to reassure. "You are safe as long as you keep their secret." Three abruptly stand and vigorously push their chairs backwards, which noisily drag along the floor as my words scrape their conscience. They leave. I search the faces of those left. Inchy lowers his face; it is pinched with fear. He quietly leaves. There are six of us left.

I change the subject and talk about Lonely Whale, Greenpeace and Sea Shepherd UK, charitable organisations that are passionate about sea and ocean conservation.

Brian takes my hand under the table and squeezes it. He says, "We should also invite the seamen and fishermen into the secret."

"Do you think that's a good idea?" asks Jerry. His phone beeps, he taps his code in then scrolls down and stops. Something is wrong—his skin is ashen and taut with vibrating puckers around

131

his mouth. He reads, voice crumbling, "The *Isle of Thanet News* has reported a boat drifting in the Channel. No one is aboard the vessel named *Salty Too*." Our eyes catch one another in recognition that it's Sally's boat. Deep sadness mingles in my stomach with the flat white.

The following day three more boats and their owners are reported missing. I did not expect this mission to end in death. Regret and disappointment wash over me, then anger. They've experienced the merfolks' magnificence. Why is that not enough? They knew what was at stake. Betrayal equals death—it's the merfolks' rule to protect their world.

As they talk, I subtly look at each person around the table. Brian I trust. I'm not sure about Jerry or Caroline, time will tell. Monty and Alice won't or can't commit to the mission but promise not to tell a soul. They wish us well and leave. There are four of us left and we have to act. Brian, Caroline and Jerry approach the fishermen in pubs and clubs. Over drinks they test out the idea of nautical tales and the merfolk—they are laughed at and ridiculed. I approach the organisations and eventually find someone who listens sincerely and is coming over to Thanet to meet me. He, Mr Merfolk, will arrange a discreet meeting party. 'No more deaths,' I silently pray to something.

\* \* \* \* \*

After an unexpected storm at sea the fishermen have a change of heart. He forewarned us so that we could be in the pub ready for when they walk in. We've got to know their names and are forging a friendship. Andrew and Bill describe, 'Crashing waves. Lightning flashes that illuminate strange people in the sea, enrobed with sea plants and shells in their long hair.'

Marty says, "As the storm subsided, the long-haired people bowed their heads and threw handfuls of old, gold coins into the boat." Andrew guffaws and chuckles, a raucous sound that reverberates in the dimly lit pub where stories hang from the beams. We laugh and drink whiskey with them; stories spin head-over-heels around the bar, along with the gold coins.

They've got it, they understand, or so I think. It transpires their comprehension is not sufficient to heed the merfolk's warning. Alec

132

and Jack gossip and gossip; they too become lost at sea during a storm. A palpitating fear hunker the seamen together in a corner of the pub, they look over at us nervously. The merfolk repeat the event, this time it permeates a deeper faculty, and the fishermen understand the privilege and the necessity of secrecy.

Over time a trust is built, and a pact drawn up—coastal sanctuaries in exchange for healthy quotas of fish. And the occasional sightings always enthral—a perfect aide memoir.

* * * * *

English ocean folklore now has a new illustrated book. He and I wrote it. The illustrations depict the merfolk as characters with special powers. Maurice is a seadog, their pet, and Captain of the puppy fish that play with the merbabies. Their stories of the past and present include the on-going battle with sea pollution and its devastation on sea-life. All profit from the book sales goes to the Friends of the Sea project set up by Lonely Whale.

* * * * *

I look back to that evening on the beach, the summer solstice when He appeared. New friendships began that were based on hope and trust, and a new alliance has been formed between those under and above the sea. New beginnings to a story that will hopefully never end.

# I STARTED WRITING WHEN ...

... I wanted to use words to create images, stories and fictional worlds.

*Anna Spain*

...I realised I could use my life experiences and knowledge to create stories which, with a bit of imagination, often turned out better than my real life and experiences.

*Anne Sikora Lord*

... I realised, instead of spending my time reading Sci-Fi and fantasy novels, I could be writing them instead.

*Carol Salter*

... I realised there were things I wanted to put in writing before they faded from memory.

*Don Munnings*

... my brain needed unclogging from all my murderous thoughts.

*Karen Hutchinson*

... I realised my mind was full of stories that I wanted to share.

*Karen Ince*

... I first learned to form letters and recognise words. I still remember my first eight-word poem: 'Fun is eating a bun in the sun'.

*Karen Leopold Reich*

... a friend suggested it might give me a break from the stresses of my job. In 2012 I began my 'literary apprenticeship' and have been writing full time since 2018.

*Lee Stoddart*

… I was a child. I never kept a diary, but I often scribbled ideas for stories, as they occurred to me.

*Mary Gumsley*

… I had free time and it was the perfect way to express thoughts, feelings, and ideas. The process of writing is relaxing and rewarding.

*Niki Sakka*

… I needed to clear my brain of nonsense.

*Shiralee Matthews*

… I was in Junior School. A teacher was impressed with one of my short stories, because I'd written 'bright pink' for a description. As of then I thoroughly enjoyed writing, because of the confidence this had given me.

*Tracey Jacobs*

… my children were young and it became clear to me how important it was to cherish memories and catch one moment in time as each is uniquely precious and not repeated.

*Valerie Tyler*

# ACKNOWLEDGEMENTS

Our thanks go to the following people:

- All the members of the group, whether their work is included in this current volume or not, who support each other, bring energy and enthusiasm to meetings, and work at developing their craft

- Those members of the group who volunteer their time and energy to run our sessions and help us to develop our knowledge

- Westgate Library for welcoming us each month in the past, and hopefully, again, in the future when it is possible.

- Carol Salter, for all her work in setting up and running the group. She's always ready to encourage each person to be the best writer they can be, and to welcome new members

- All members of the group who helped with critiquing the writing included here

- Karen Ince for copy-editing and formatting the collection, and for the cover design.

- Photograph by Wesley Tingey on Unsplash used in creation of front cover